What Science Knows About Life

WHAT SCIENCE KNOWS

DR. HEINZ WOLTERECK

translated by MERVYN SAVILL

Association Press, New York

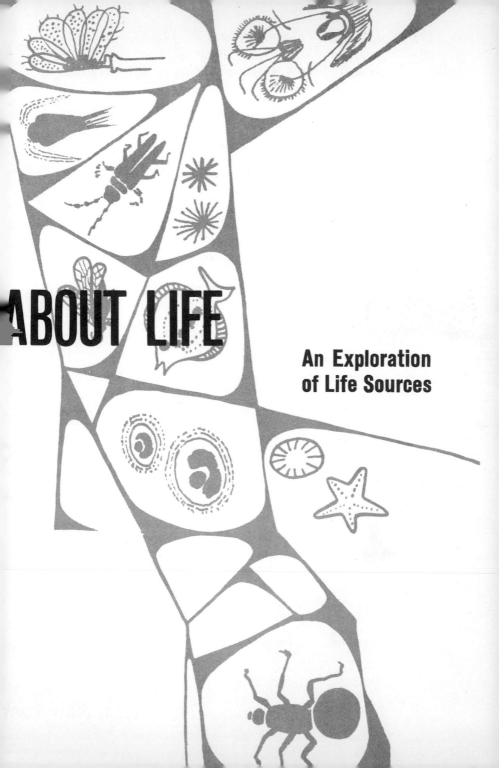

ABOUT LIFE

An Exploration
of Life Sources

Table of Contents

Illustrations

ix

CHAPTER I

Life in the Universe

WE love to cherish illusions—and this also holds good in science. Some of these illusions are surprisingly long-lived: they can survive for centuries. Ever since man began to wonder about himself and his position in the universe, ever since he tried to unravel the secret of life, his findings right down to modern times have been far too flattering to himself. Let us examine them briefly. At the outset these reflections produced curious notions such as the "cosmic egg", which has undergone the oddest twists since about the 4th century B.C. (It was observed that life invariably began with the egg, and man translated this experience to the universe.) The ancient Indians and Chinese both believed the universe to be a gigantic egg, the white forming the sky, the yolk the earth, with the water in between. Later followed the first "scientific" conceptions, the realities of which were not much greater.

The Greek scholar Thales of Miletus and his no less famous pupil, Anaximander, explained the firmament as a huge crystal bell which at the creation was spread over the earth like an umbrella. Then came the astronomer Ptolemaeus, whom we have to thank for admirable calculations of the solar and lunar eclipses. His cosmic system naturally placed the earth at the centre of the universe. There it remained in the opinion of competent scholars until the year 1543, when Copernicus banished the earth, and with it man, from its all too flattering role. "Possibly no greater challenge has ever been offered to man," was Goethe's comment on this event. Giordano Bruno, however, died at the stake for upholding the same dangerous claim, and Galileo had to recant, for he too would have been burned had he continued to voice these unwelcome truths.

Today every schoolchild knows that from a cosmic standpoint our earth is an insignificant planet in orbit round a normal star on the fringe of one of the innumerable Milky Ways.

(It has been estimated that there are 100,000 million stars in our Milky Way alone.) Looked at in this light, the age-old and subconsciously never entirely abandoned claim of man to be lord of the earth and the crowning glory of creation has long since ceased to have any validity. But another verdict of modern astronomy seemed at least to give some justification for the claim. Life appeared to be a very rare and special phenomenon in the universe. The British astronomer Sir James Jeans, in several of his works, published figures showing that even in the course of many billions of years the chances of the creation of a solar system were not even 100,000 to one. Now the age of the universe is estimated at only a few thousand million years. The well-known viewpoint of Jeans and other leading astronomers and astrophysicists therefore had a very flattering inference for mankind. The existence of planets was considered to be exceptional. Were a heavenly body, like the earth, to afford the possibility for the development of higher life—and eventually man—then, according to Jeans, it was an exceedingly rare phenomenon. *Homo sapiens*, in the critical 20th century, found his exceptional position in the universe confirmed once more.

But Jeans was little concerned with this in his calculations. He was advancing a credible and very illuminating theory on the origin of the planets, no more no less. It was based on the premise that the creation of our planetary system was the result of a highly improbable cosmic accident. In the remote past a star, sweeping very close to the sun, tore from it a long stream of molten gases. The cloud of gas split into a train of particles which began, because of its gravitational pull, to circle the sun, forming the "material" of which the planets were ultimately composed. This theory seemed plausible, but as a result of further observations and calculations it has proved to be incorrect. Jeans made a mistake. The origin of the planets was not as he had envisaged. In all probability our sun was originally a rotating cloud of gas, from which large masses of gas constantly spurted, forming a kind of disc, the sun being at the centre. At certain places accumulations of these erupted atoms of the heavy elements formed, resulting in gigantic condensation masses: these were the proto-planets. After an incalculable length of time these proto-planets grew denser by contraction until a system of solid bodies ultimately evolved—the planets in their present-day form.

From this evidence we can draw a very important conclusion, namely that the formation of a planetary system is by no means exceptional but quite a normal occurrence in the universe. Specific proof is naturally difficult because the planets of other normal stars cannot be seen, even through the most powerful telescopes. There are, however, indirect methods of observation. With quite modest instruments certain disturbances, which are undoubtedly caused by the gravitational pull of planets, can be observed round the nearer fixed stars. The astronomer H. Shapley recently drew the relevant biological corollaries from our newly-won knowledge with extraordinarily interesting results. For the first time he used a statistical method to arrive at the minimal figure for the frequency of life-bearing planets. His basic premise was that only one out of 1,000 suns possesses a planetary system. The acceptable maximal figure would be in the ratio of 1 : 50. But since many of the planets in orbit are undoubtedly inimical to life Shapley used an eliminatory method of calculation, taking into account all the conditions essential to life on a planet. (We shall return later to this very important question.) To be on the safe side Shapley worked in four successive stages. As we have already mentioned, only one out of 1,000 normal stars possesses planets. Now we can accept that only one out of every 1,000 planetary systems fulfils the "required distance" between the sun and the planet. Again, in each of these 1,000 systems only one single planet will be the right size and have the right atmosphere. Among these 1,000 that fulfil all the requirements, the surface of only one will be suited to the development of life.

This is admittedly a very cautious calculation and one which takes every unfavourable possibility into account. Nevertheless it gives the remarkable result that in the universe at least 100 million planets afford possibilities favourable to the development of life. Shapley's method may be too pessimistic for it employs the very high safety margin of 1 : 1,000. It would be reasonable to reduce this safety margin to 1 : 100, but this is hardly necessary. Any conservative calculation, at the present-day state of our knowledge, shows that life is a normal phenomenon in the universe. We know that it is not unique as was previously believed. To sum up: our sun is a normal star and there are hosts of stars similar to it in all respects. Among their number there must be many that have developed planetary systems similar to our own.

IS THERE LIFE ON MARS AND VENUS?

With all its robustness and ability to adapt itself to unfavourable conditions, life is bound by a series of requirements without which it cannot exist. We have already referred to these and it is now time to examine this important factor more closely. The first essential is a certain range of temperature—the most favourable being between 0° and 104° F. Intense cold can be endured by various forms of life, at least for a given period; intense heat, on the other hand, is absolutely pathogenic. Neither the sun nor any other star can entertain even the most elementary bacteria, for their surfaces have a temperature of several thousand degrees Fahrenheit. In consequence the planets, and possibly their satellites, are the only refuges of life. A long series of specific conditions must also be fulfilled before any type of life can develop on a planet. A solid crust of suitable form must be available, together with a sufficiently dense atmosphere and enough water. These are the basic prerequisites.

Man has always been curious to know whether life exists on other planets in our solar system. What are the possibilities?

Our own satellite, the moon, on account of its small mass, has not enough gravitational pull to maintain an atmosphere. When the first space-ship lands on the moon the astronauts will find neither water nor air. The temperature conditions, too, will be extremely unfavourable—at night —302° F, and by day a ground temperature of more than 212° F. The visitor to the moon will therefore have to wear specially designed protective clothing, and a prolonged stay will entail great hardship. Due to the lack of an atmosphere, communication will be confined to the telephone because sound waves can be transmitted only through air. Without air no fire will kindle and no combustion engine will function. In works of science fiction we read how easy it is to move about on the moon, its surface gravity being only one-sixth that of the earth, but man is geared to the gravity of our earth and in the long run this reduction might prove very uncomfortable.

To these drawbacks must be added inconceivably bright sunshine and dangerous quantities of cosmic radiation. In short, a trip to the moon would be a very unpleasant excursion. A stay there would be possible only in specially equipped chambers, transported by the astronauts themselves. Their inmates would be the only living creatures on our inhospitable satellite. From certain colour changes at various spots on the moon's surface the Russian scientist Kosirev suspects the presence of a primitive vegetation (algæ), but so far this is merely a hypothesis. Kosirev thinks that the existence of such plants could be made possible by gases (carbon dioxide) rising out of the crevices of the giant moon craters. This question will not be answered until the first lunar expedition has landed on the satellite.

The planets of our solar system can be divided into two groups—the inner planets of the earth type (these include Mars and Venus) and the outer planets (Jupiter, Saturn, Uranus and Neptune). Although the "Martians", and the canals accredited to them, are a recurrent topic of discussion there is not the slightest prospect of such fantasies proving true. Mars of course has certain features in common with the earth: it has seasons and an atmosphere, although the latter is very thin and dry. But there is very little water on Mars and the prevailing temperatures are unfavourable to the development of higher life for in the warmest regions the midday temperature rises to more than 86° F and falls to −212° F at night. Compared with the latter condition the climate at the top of Mount Everest would be mild. Without protective clothing a man could not survive so low a temperature for ten minutes.

Nevertheless a very sparse vegetation appears to thrive, because observations show that large regions change colour during the course of the year. In the Martian winter they appear brownish, changing quite clearly to green in the summer. This vegetation probably consists of lichens and algæ, and to recent observers seems to resemble that of the Arctic tundra. All possibilities for the existence of higher life on Mars can be ruled out.

Our beautiful morning and evening star, Venus, is similar

to the earth in shape and size, but living conditions on this planet are very different from our own and it is improbable that a space-ship will ever be able to land there. Science would welcome such a landing since Venus is perpetually shrouded in a dense covering of cloud which even the most powerful telescopes cannot penetrate. This cloud reflects the intense solar radiation on the surface and is responsible for the extremely high temperatures reigning there. (Venus is about 25 million miles nearer to the sun than the earth). According to the latest calculations the midday temperature on Venus rises to 572° F; during the night it apparently drops to near freezing point. Its atmosphere consists in the main of carbon dioxide, a little water vapour, but practically no oxygen. In all these circumstances it would seem that Venus, in its present state, is incapable of entertaining any form of higher life.

None of the remaining planets of our solar system can be considered as supporters of life. Mercury is a stony desert without a trace of atmosphere; and the outer planets, Jupiter, Saturn, Uranus and Neptune, are so far from the sun that they are too cold for even the most primitive forms of life. On Jupiter, for example, the daily temperature is about −266° F and its atmosphere contains poisonous gases such as methane and ammonia, partly in solid form. No possible chance, then, of life. . . .

We arrive at the following balance sheet. In our solar system only the earth can guarantee higher life. On Mars there are presumably lower forms of plant life but no animals—let alone "Martians". All the remaining planets are uninhabitable.

THE SPECIAL CASE OF THE EARTH

We human beings are lucky to live on a planet which, with apologies to Leibniz, has been termed "the best of all possible worlds". A whole series of factors combined to create these essentially favourable conditions to the development of higher life, and ultimately man. While on the remaining planets of our solar system it is either too hot or too cold, in the most important regions of the earth's surface the "right" temperatures, between 0° F and 104° F, are the norm. This is primarily because the position of our planet with regard to the sun is very favourable to the development of life; its distance from the heat-giving central star allows the latter's radiated energy to produce the right surface temperature for the greater part of the earth. The earth's swift rotation sees to it that the regions subjected to the strongest solar radiation do not have to endure this too long but can cool off during the night.

Another very important factor is the inclination of the earth's axis. Were this axis at right-angles to its path round the sun, we should have no seasons and no modification of the climatic conditions existing at the poles and the equator. Large tracts of the earth's surface which are today habitable would have a climate hostile to life. Were the axis, on the other hand, to lie on the plane of the orbit, things would be even worse for us: one half of the globe would endure almost perpetual night and icy cold, while the climate on the other half would at all times be unbearably hot. Both extremes would be equally fatal. Scientists have calculated the ideal axial position to provide the most favourable conditions for life on earth, and an interesting fact emerged. The optimal conditions are an inclination of the earth's axis of between 23° and 24°. The earth's actual inclination is $23\frac{1}{2}$°.

A further imperative condition for all life is the existence of a suitably composed atmosphere. Here again the earth is particularly favoured. Up to an altitude of about 6 miles we find the air to consist of approximately 78% nitrogen, 21% oxygen, 1% argon and 0·03% carbonic acid, together with small amounts of hydrogen, neon and helium. Apart from this the air contains water vapour which is subject to great quantitative changes. The life of plants and animals, as we know, depends above all on oxygen and carbon dioxide, both of which are used in a marvellous "division of work" by the various groups of the earth's inhabitants. With the aid of oxygen, by combustion (oxidation) of foods, men and animals obtain their life energy, the end-products of this synthesis being carbon dioxide and water. Conversely, by photogenesis, plants break down the carbon dioxide in the air, thereby producing the basic material of all organic combinations, carbon. By this well-known assimilation oxygen is once more produced and the wheel comes full circle. Were our atmosphere to contain no oxygen or carbonic acid, higher life as we know it would be impossible.

Life is further protected from other dangers by the atmosphere. The latter constitutes an effective armour against the constant bombardment from outer space. Meteorites of all sizes hurtle into our atmosphere at the fantastic speed of 37,000–93,000 m.p.h. Taking into account only the small and smallest "shooting stars", it has been calculated that about 10 million of these projectiles are fired at our planet in the course of 24 hours. The protective armour of the atmosphere wards them off. Most of the meteorites burn up as they enter the atmosphere and reach the earth as harmless dust. Only against outsize "missiles" does the air afford no protection, but these very rarely cause damage. They fall to the earth as a "rain of stones" or lumps of metal. That a monk was once struck by a meteorite in the streets of Milan, or that many years ago one set fire to the Paris Law Courts, must be looked upon as freak occurrences. On the whole, life is safe from this bombardment of small cosmic splinters, which we see in the night sky as balls of fire or shooting stars. Only really large meteorites can pierce the envelope of the atmosphere, with the power to cause great damage should they fall on a city. Many years ago a giant meteorite fell in Arizona, making a crater some 550 ft. deep and 4,000 ft. in diameter. Another that fell in the Siberian wastes on 30th June, 1908, destroyed a huge tract of virgin forest. But as we have said, such "rogues" are the exception and occur perhaps once in a century.

Of far greater importance, in fact a basic condition for the creation and preservation of life on the earth, is the protection afforded by the atmosphere against harmful radiation. The air acts as a giant sieve, allowing only a certain quantity of the rays to pass through, while others are completely or partially warded off. The deadly ultra-short rays hardly reach us at all —and it is precisely this radiation which has a deleterious effect on most organisms. Nor do the cosmic rays from outer space, capable of penetrating a thick steel plate, reach the earth except in a reduced quantity not fatal to life. Only 0·6% of the radiation measured in the stratosphere (19 miles up) reaches the earth.

And finally, the well-known fact must be mentioned that the atmosphere *a priori* makes possible the climatic conditions suitable for life. It filters and distributes the sunlight in the most favourable manner, bringing about a levelling of temperature differences by a "glasshouse effect" and distributing the life-giving water over the earth's surface. By its circulation it serves as a constant conductor of heat, with the result that large areas of the earth enjoy far more favourable conditions than solar radiation alone would provide. In this way the area available for life is greatly increased.

WE ARE NOT ALONE IN THE UNIVERSE

Man's claim to have reached the highest stage, at least in "his" solar system, still holds good, but the significance of this statement must not be over-estimated. Our solar system lies at the edge of a gigantic cosmic configuration. We can see its further reaches in the clear night sky as the pale shimmer of the Milky Way. The whole Milky Way is a "cosmic island" known to astronomers as a galaxy. The centre of this system, which surpasses imagination, is some 15,000 light years away from us. (A light year is the distance travelled by light in one year: it represents 590 billion miles.) The total size of this vast structure is a matter of guesswork, but a diameter of 100,000 light years has been suggested. The system has the shape of a huge spiral disc. This, then, is a rough picture of our universe, but there are many more galaxies and other spiral nebulæ—1½ million light years separate us from the nearest of the latter, the nebula in Andromeda. And man once thought that his insignificant earth was the centre of the universe!

In the light of modern knowledge it would be a gross error to imagine that our earth has a monopoly in developing life. On whichever side Shapley's calculations err, we are certainly not alone in the universe. It is built on a single principle and the laws which govern life hold good throughout it. We shall deal with this question in the next chapter. For the moment let us see whether science has any proofs to help us determine how life might appear on other planets in other systems.

According to the astronomer Fred Hoyle there are a million planets in our own Milky Way whose physio-chemical conditions are approximately the same as those of the earth. Shapley suggests that, given the basic requirements for the development of life and sufficiently long periods of time, plants and animals would be born with at least some features in common with their terrestrial counterparts. Were it in our power to visit other planets which correspond to our own in age, composition, temperature, etc., says Shapley, we should probably find that their biology would be within the scope of our understanding. The geneticist Darlington goes one step further. He does not find it incredible that there should be men-like creatures somewhere in outer space. His argument is illuminating. "Since great advantages are gained by walking on two legs, by having a brain in the head, two eyes in the same plane and a height of about 5 feet, we must accept the possibility that other planets are inhabited by living creatures who resemble us physically."

There are of course other possibilities. For life on earth certain chemical elements are essential—in the main carbon, oxygen, hydrogen and sulphur. From these elements are composed the actual building materials of the living substance, i.e. the proteins. It is not impossible that other "methods" could produce the living substance. For example, the carbon could be replaced by silica. This would provide different material for the organism and the living beings would in all probability bear no resemblance to humans. If, according to Shapley's "minimal" figure, there are at least 100 million inhabited planets —in reality there are probably far more—then forms of life completely unknown to us are conceivable. It would naturally be of the greatest interest to observe such alien organisms, but unfortunately the chances of so doing are remote. The nearest fixed star, Proxima Centauri, is 4·2 light years away, a distance which could not be covered with present-day rocket fuel.

Some space travel theoreticians believe that sooner or later it will be possible to build so-called photon rockets. They would be driven by the energy of light and could therefore reach speeds in the neighbourhood of the speed of light (ca. 187,000 m. per second). Whether this will ever become practical is a matter of doubt. But there would be other insuperable difficulties. The human body would be subjected to appalling strain from the incredible acceleration needed to reach such speeds. This would be repeated when the rocket, shortly before reaching its destination, had to brake in order to land. It is also doubtful whether the astronauts would ever be able to see a hitherto uncharted planet as they sped past it. Since it reflects only the light of its own sun it would hardly be spotted in time at the speed the space-ship would be travelling. Again, taking into account the risk of landing on a planet and taking off again for home, there seems no chance of realising such a project in the light of our present-day knowledge and techniques. For a long time yet we shall have to remain in our own solar system.

On the other hand, most scientists are convinced that within a foreseeable time the first interplanetary space-ship will leave our earth. The crew may be Russian or American and the launching may be next week or in ten years' time, but it will assuredly take place. The candidates are ready; they have been whirled about in compression chambers, subjected to enormous pressures, artificial weightlessness, and other physical strains. But the finest standards in this field are not enough; mental and spiritual qualities must also be present. The latest experiments in America have proved this.

In a space-ship the crew will be constricted in movement. During the flight there will be little of interest to do. Human hand movements and reactions for steering the speedy craft will be inadequate. Navigational details and commands will be given by electronic brains coupled directly to the automatic steering device. The astronauts will have practically nothing to do for days and weeks on end except watch the instruments, take readings, and perform certain tasks at given intervals. It was found that even hardened candidates flagged after a few days. They began to see strange colours, to hear unreal noises and to have hallucinations. They became deaf. Space flight doctors explain such phenomena as a defence mechanism of the human system. In order to function properly the brain in fact needs constant stimuli transmitted to it by the sensory organs. When these are inadequate the brain artificially replaces them with "falsifications". The danger such monotonous conditions will entail for the crews is clear. Professor Trumbull, official psychiatrist to the American Navy, has devised a detailed pro-gramme to solve the problem. All members of a space-ship crew must have their faculties intelligently employed during all waking hours. In addition to their routine work they will study a language or some technical or scientific subject. A non-stop "space entertainment programme" will be relayed, with films, gramophone records, or variety.

But there is still something more important: members of the

crew must get along with each other under the most trying circumstances. The American Air Force has collected some instructive information from the first experiments in this field.
A crew of young airmen, who had come through all their pre-
liminary tests with flying colours, lived for five days in a replica
of a space-cabin. They slept eight hours out of twenty-four,
remained awake for the other sixteen, and spent fifteen minutes
of each hour on some specific task. At first they were quite
happy and there were endless discussions on all manner of
topics. The prescribed work was carried out admirably. But
the longer their enforced company lasted the weaker grew their
contact. There were quarrels, work was carried out inefficiently,
and towards the end of the experiment the men had only one
thing in common—meals. From these experiments, it appeared
to be essential that the astronaut be courageous, self-reliant
and highly intelligent; have a calm temperament and the power
to remain unruffled; and, above all, be a "good mixer" and
able to get on well with his mates and stand by them when
things go badly.

In this connection American experts studied the question of
women scientists taking part in space travel. The reply was in
the affirmative. There is a strong foundation for this. Doctors
and psychiatrists know from experience that mentally and physically the woman is in many respects far tougher than the
man and has greater powers of resistance in adversity. Women
are comparatively insensitive to monotony, they can stand
boring jobs better than men, and could come to terms better
with such inconveniences as the restricted quarters in a space-
ship. Were the right women chosen, they might, with feminine
instinct, be able to overcome the difficulties of the men taking
part, for weeks on end, in a "voyage through the universe".

Man's conception of the world has expanded. We know today that our entire solar system is a mere speck in an inconceivably vast cosmos. There are a host of "archipelagos" in space: our photograph shows one of these, the spiral nebula in the Great Bear. On how many of them does life exist?

Diatoms from New Zealand.

Diatomeus campylodicus.

This sea lily lived in the Jurassic, about 150 million years ago, and was quarried from a limestone cliff. It is not a plant but an animal, actually an echinoderm. Several species of this primitive group, the so-called *crinoidae*, have survived.

CHAPTER II

How Did Life Originate?

FOR more than 2,000 years man has been trying to discover the secret of life and its origins. This is the famous question of "spontaneous generation", the first and oldest problem in natural science. Man has always wanted to know how it was possible that living creatures formed on our planet. They could not in any case have been indigenous to the earth, could not have been there "beforehand", because we know that for a long period conditions ruled which were completely inimical to life. In its initial stages our planet was an incandescent ball of fire, formed of the same cosmic gases as the sun. Being a million times smaller than the latter—1,300,000 earths would find room in the sun—it must have cooled rapidly in the cold of space. A firm crust formed, consolidating in the course of time, losing its original heat and at the same time affording an opportunity for the seething masses of steam surrounding the young star to condense in the form of water. The first proto-ocean appeared, continents emerged, and in the stormy travail of upheaval and subsidence a still far from stable surface formed in that immeasurably distant past, finally revealing the face of our mother earth. The development continued for millions of years, rivers and seas working as they do today, eroding the firm rock of the earth's crust. They created mighty deposits of stratified sediment on the sea bed and the continents. Slowly, incredibly slowly to the conception of short-lived man, order was introduced into the cataclysmic chaos of that stormy springtime of the earth. The swirling mists of water vapour dissolved, and finally the day came when for the first time bright sunshine lay over a planet which, in addition to continents and seas, possessed an envelope of atmosphere. At this stage the first prerequisites for the development of life were to hand.

But how did this possibility become fact? In the past the answer did not seem particularly difficult. It was generally observed how the lowlier living creatures were, as it were, generated spontaneously—frogs in the newly-dried pools, maggots in rotting meat, vermin in filth, etc. It seemed quite clear, therefore, that toads and frogs originated from mud, maggots from meat, and vermin from filth. Aristotle explains in detail how these various forms of spontaneous generation occurred—eels, for example, formed from worms and the latter merely from mud. Today we laugh at such crazy notions, but there is every cause to fear that the schoolboy, in a hundred years' time, will laugh just as heartily at some of our own scientific ideas.

It took a very long time before mankind began to cast doubts on the Aristotelian theory of spontaneous generation. As late as the 16th century it was still accepted that young mice originated from flour and dirty linen—had they not actually been seen? Gradually a few of the major errors were cleared up, but even a hundred years later the Italian scientist Redi had bitter disputes with his colleagues when he dared to demonstrate that the Aristotelian theory of the spontaneous generation of fly maggots was false. Redi's experiment was simple enough. He cut a piece of meat in two halves, letting one piece lie exposed to the air and covering the other with fine muslin. Naturally the maggots only developed in the piece of meat which was exposed to the flies. But it was some time before his experiment was recognised.

At length, as a result of countless observations of the true circumstances, the old theory of spontaneous generation in the case of mice, toads, insects, etc., was finally discarded. But in the 19th century it was resurrected, this time at a deeper level —viz. in the realm of bacteria. In 1675 the Dutchman Anthony van Leeuwenhoek had seen bacteria for the first time in a piece of dental tartar with the aid of a lens he had himself polished. People quarrelled for almost 200 years as to the nature of these tiny living creatures. They were to be met with everywhere in their myriads—in the air, in the earth, in water, and in proximity to men and animals. When Pasteur discovered the yeast bacillus, whose activities curdle the milk and turn butter rancid and wine sour, the supporters of spontaneous generation once more had ground to stand on. Where did these tiny ubiquitous "microbes" come from except from decaying matter itself?

In the 18th century the Italian Spallanzani, in carefully conceived experiments, had shown the fallacy of bacterial autogeny without being able to convince the partisans of this theory. Pasteur, a passionate and aggressive fighter, now threw himself into the bitter controversy. For many years, in a small room of the Ecole Normale in Paris (it is still visited today by respectful tourists) he carried out countless experiments in this field. After sterilising various decaying substances by boiling, he left part of them exposed and hermetically sealed the remainder. It invariably happened that the most heterogeneous substances decayed on exposure to the air while they underwent no change when properly sealed. Pasteur could triumphantly prove to his opponents, and in particular to his great rival Pouchet, that the bacteria surrounding the substances of his experiments were obviously contained in the air. When Robert Koch, a little later, described the genesis of the anthrax bacillus with great accuracy and detail in his famous work the theory of bacterial spontaneous generation was finally abandoned. The "microbe hunters" found one disease bacillus after another, and in the last ten years of the 19th and the beginning of the 20th century natural science forged ahead. Ever new riddles, which had remained unsolved for centuries, were now solved with a wave of the hand. It must therefore have been within the bounds of possibility that men were at last on the verge of discovering the secret of life itself!

A SLIGHT ERROR CONCERNING "PRIMEVAL SLIME"

The mechanistic age in natural science had dawned. With its continued successes in all fields, it appeared to have found its confirmation at last. Ernst Haeckel and his "progressive" colleagues set out to solve the remaining problems of Nature with test-tube and microscope. Soon it appeared that there would no longer be a "mystery of life" but only plain, crystal-clear, and calculable facts in the light of an all-explaining science. And what of spontaneous generation? After a series of setbacks in this field Haeckel and others had grown rather more modest. In their opinion it was not the complete but the so-called partially animate forerunners of life only—the probionta—that created themselves out of inorganic matter. Only gradually and in the course of evolution did true living creatures develop from these elementary stages. This theory, as we shall see, still holds good in principle today, but in its original form it was far too elementary to stand up to the actual facts. The problem had been over-simplified by biologists, who believed that they would soon be in a position to manufacture the first living creature in the laboratory, completely overlooking one basic fact—that life is not matter but a process. How incredibly complicated and almost inconceivable to the human mind this life process is we will discuss in the next chapter. Here we propose merely to illustrate the over-optimistic attitude of the mechanists of that period.

Haeckel and others, on well-founded grounds, postulated the formation of the first probionta as being in the sea, where they constantly reproduced themselves by spontaneous generation. It is easy to understand what a triumph it was for the biologists of that day when an oceanographic expedition brought up from the sea bed the primeval slime, the alleged first stage of spontaneous generation. It was in fact a strange substance of a slimy nature which in aspect and character turned out to be quite different from the substance they had envisaged lifeless matter to be. The famous British naturalist Thomas Huxley examined the find very carefully and published his sensational findings. "In the slime the simplest form of living matter, which developed out of dead matter on the sea bed, has actually been found." In Haeckel's honour this protozoon was called *Bathybius Hæckelii*.

The news of the discovery was like a bombshell in the world of scientists. It seemed that at last the decisive missing link between "living" and "dead" had been found, and with it an irrefutable confirmation of the theories fashionable at the time. Unfortunately the case of *Bathybius Hæckelii* turned out later to be based on a "slight error". It was neither a living creature nor the primitive stage of one, but merely ordinary inorganic salts! The reason this was not immediately discovered was because they were not in their usual form. The salts were so-called colloids and their formlessness, due to this chemical condition, accounted for Huxley's error.

Bathybius Hæckelii was a fiasco. Nor were the other theories of probionta satisfactory in their old form. This applied equally to the Fechner school, which considered the earth itself to be an organism from which inorganic particles fell in solid form during the period of cooling; life, on the other hand, being in liquid and gaseous form. From these animated constituent parts protoplasm, the actual material of true living substance, was formed in the course of time. As to how this was possible the theory did not explain. Such points of view merely begged the actual basic question, the issue at stake being how living substance can or could have been built from the inanimate. Several other theories of spontaneous generation existed—they are still accepted by certain authors—but they were all too far-fetched to mention in this work. They are all the more easily rejected since the latest researches have enabled us to approach the fantastically difficult problem of the origins of life with the most modern methods and to make at least a plausible con-jecture. They are still the first tentative steps, and so far we have lifted only a small fringe of the veil with which Nature has so effectively shrouded this mystery. But we have at least a point of departure from which to work, and experimental research has begun, as opposed to obscure theories each of which by and large was more contrived and impossible to prove than the next.

IT BEGAN WITH A MOLECULE

Theories of spontaneous generation were apt to be associated with phenomena which had not been examined fundamentally enough. Prior to Redi's experiments, little was known of worms and parasites, little of bacteria before the discoveries of Pasteur and Koch, and as a result errors as to their origin and signi-ficance could quite easily occur. Later research furnished a certain parallel in the field of viruses. The "invisible" viruses were first recognised with the aid of the electron microscope. Their examination was extremely difficult, and moreover they behaved both as "living" and "dead" material. An attempt was therefore made with the aid of viruses to revive the old theory of spontaneous generation in a modern guise—but the virus is a parasite relying on the existence of higher life, and thus it is impossible that it could have existed *ab initio*. This was the last in a long series of attempts to regard "complete" organisms, at ever lower levels (frogs, maggots, bacteria, viruses), as being products of spontaneous generation. No further theories of this nature will be advanced, for overwhelming evidence has taught us that in order to answer the vital question "How did life begin?" we must start at the bottom to find a solution. It lies in a world of the smallest dimensions. The molecule, capable of reproduction, stands at the foot of the inconceivably long and difficult path which ultimately led to the creation of the first living creatures.

In order to appreciate the modern viewpoint we must review once more the initial situation and conditions under which the very first forms of life could leave their imprint on our planet. The situation arose at the formation of a firm land surface and an expanse of temperate ocean. The earth's crust had been cooled and eroded by the ceaseless downpours from the forming atmosphere on to the primeval rock, and at the same time by rivers and oceans. Fertile mineral mud was deposited on the sea bed, the mainland or littoral now giving the earth for the first time in its history the possibility of harbouring life. It is immaterial whether the first forms of life originated in the sea slime itself or on its shores, nor does this affect the question of spontaneous generation. Theoretically, then, how could the first forms of life have been created? If we follow the fossil chain of known forms of life through the various geological periods we observe a progressive sequence, from simple to highly organised creations. The earliest traces of life known to us from the pre-Cambrian are simple organisms, so it is logical to assume that the first stages of the protozoa must have been far more primitive—molecules.

When the earth cooled, completely different conditions ruled from those we know today. The atmosphere contained little or no oxygen, consisting in the main of methane, ammonia, carbon dioxide and water vapour. This proto-atmosphere was subject to continuous severe thunderstorms. Although this has been common knowledge for a long time, the attempt to reconstruct these conditions artificially in the laboratory was a new departure towards discovering the origins of life. In the vanguard were the American scientists, notably Professors Miller and MacNevin. For their purpose they built a special apparatus to bombard with electric charges a mixture of gas corresponding to the proto-atmosphere of the earth. If their assumptions were correct, the basic building material of the living substance, proteins—i.e. the amino-acids—must form. The results of the experiment came amazingly close to expectations. After a week the structurally complex amino-acids had formed in the apparatus. Since then similar experiments have been carried out by scientists all over the world and their findings correspond closely to those of their American colleagues.

It was the beginning of work which has recently led to further significant successes. We must now describe briefly the conclusions to be drawn from the above experiments. Millions of years ago amino-acids formed in the proto-atmosphere; they rained down on the oceans, seas, shallow bays and lagoons. Here, in the most "favourable" places, further transformations of amino-acids into protein compounds of the most infinite variety took place down the ages. This was the initial stage of a purely chemical synthesis of organic material on our planet. Millions of years passed before the formation of the first and most primitive forms of life. The age of the earth is estimated at between 4 and $4\frac{1}{2}$ thousand million years, but the first identifiable traces of life date only from the late pre-Cambrian —i.e. 6 to 7 hundred million years ago.

Endless time. An inconceivable number of "experimental stations" for future life in water and mud. Here and there conditions were exceptionally favourable, with the result that the proteins amalgamated in tiny droplets. Ever more complex combinations ensued until, at a given moment, something new occurred: a construction of this type divided and reproduction began. The Russian biologist, Professor Oparin, was able to reproduce in his laboratory this theoretically extremely rare phenomenon. He had experimented for years on the same lines as his colleagues Miller and MacNevin, and was finally able to observe that in certain cases the protein droplets divided like bacteria.

LIFE FROM THE LIFELESS

Such protein droplets were naturally only models of those chemically produced in the primeval slime—the originals which to some degree provided the material for the initial stages of life—but for the first time in his history man can obtain by exact experiment demonstrable evidence of how

"living" orginated from "dead" material. Initially, in certain
suitable localities, organic compounds were formed from inorganic material, among them proteins. In particularly favourable circumstances these could amalgamate into larger constructions. A certain elementary structure, and the rudiments
of what we call in the biological sense individuality, are to be
found in such concentrations of organic molecules. Even at
this early stage we can observe the principle of selection subsequently found throughout Nature, an effective measure to
ensure the survival of the most successful products.

For these fortuitous forerunners of life there naturally existed
a host of possibilities for chemical synthesis with the material
of their environment. According to conditions, varying from
case to case, inorganic and organic materials could be absorbed
in the already formed structures. The "best" of them gradually
developed to higher systems of increasing perfection. They
remained stable, whereas the so-to-speak unsuccessful combinations, together with their protein molecules, disappeared
or were superseded by selection in favour of the better. Of the
countless purely chance constructions of this type, formed by
chemical contact with the materials of their environment, in
the long run only those survived which could show particularly
favourable chemical combinations, giving them not only a
chance of survival but of "reproduction". This term cannot
be taken here in the biological context, for in these initial
stages all the prerequisites for life were lacking. It was in fact
a multiplication of certain molecules in a physio-chemical
"milieu" with the co-operation of the so-called catalysts.

This scientific word is so vital that we must examine it more
closely. By catalysis we mean a whole complex of processes
originating from a certain form of chemical stimulus. The
"stimulators" or catalysts possess the strange feature of hasten-
ing a number of chemical and physical reactions by their
presence, and of making possible their multiplication. They
themselves are unimpaired by the stimuli they arouse and can
therefore continue to cause new reactions, at the expense of an
insignificant amount of catalysing substance. Our modern
chemical industry employs catalysts such as platinum, ferric
oxide, etc., in a host of products. The industry can partially dispense with the co-operation of these catalysts, but life itself cannot.

We shall constantly return to the activities of the bio-catalysts, which are so inextricably bound up with countless biological processes. For example, they regulate the digestive system. Catalysts undoubtedly existed during the initial stages of life, for they constituted one of its most important aids. A certain group of bio-catalysts, the ferments, have been nick-named rather poetically but appropriately "Nature's quick-eners". When life originated catalysts undoubtedly partici-pated in a decisive manner, particularly in the shape of a special variety known as auto-catalysts. Here ingenious Nature exploited a positively brilliant idea: the introduction of processes in which the "hastener", the catalyst, was in a posi-tion to stimulate itself. By this incredible back somersault in the chemistry of biology it transpired that the required effect became at the same time its own cause. Expressed differently: in the last analysis the catalysed end-product contributed to its own creation.

Oparin and others were able to prove that the previously mentioned "selection" in the primary amalgamation of the protein molecules present in primeval slime depended on these simultaneously formed auto-catalysts. The proto-structures of the protein molecule with the best chance of becoming stable and of reproducing were those in which the most perfect fer-ments of the auto-catalytic type could be created as a result of specially favourable combinations of material. In 1955 Oparin proved by laboratory experiment that in individual cases and in given circumstances regular division takes place in the pro-tein droplets under the influence of spontaneously formed fer-ments. This, therefore, was the primary stage in the genuine reproduction of a bacterium.

The well-known German research worker Pascual Jordan points to a fact which further enhances the presumption of "spontaneous generation" in the sense described—viz. the fact that relatively few "living molecules", resulting from spon-taneous generation, would have been enough to introduce the development of life on earth. Modern genetics, by the study of so-called mutations (natural or artificially induced changes in the inherited structure of organisms, which will be trans-mitted) has been able again and again to show that in certain circumstances whole races and populations can originate from single individuals. It is a known fact, for example, that all the double petunias that bloom in our gardens today are descended from a single specimen. In a Parisian garden in 1885 a double petunia blossomed by chance from a single variety through mutation—it was the ancestor of countless generations of these lovely flowers.

It is therefore quite possible that the formation of the first "living molecules" was merely a remarkable coincidence. Once present, they could, by auto-catalysis, have reproduced with avalanche proportions and could have formed the first broad lower stratum on which, in the course of æons, the further development of life was based. On the strength of his researches into the protein molecules, Jordan came to the conclusion that the chemical structure of the first protein molecule of this type could be forecast with a certain degree of probability.

We can safely leave the solution of these individual problems to future research, but another basic question of interest still arises: from the inexhaustible potential for chemical reactions in the primeval slime, how did the specific formation of a protein molecule, capable of reproduction through auto-catalysis, actually occur? Was it pure chance or was it more than this? We can at least give a certain, even if necessarily partial, reply upon critical examination of the course of the spontaneous generation theories. As we have already seen, higher life, such as frogs, insects, etc., were presumed to have formed on their own; the same capacity was then accredited to the more simply built bacteria, and finally to the viruses. All these theories placed the disengagement of the living substance from inorganic material at a far too advanced stage of its development. The first spark of life could not glimmer in the world of macrophysics—i.e. of visible phenomena (visible also under the microscope)—because the difference between it and the far more primitive inorganic world was far too great. Man, in his quest for the secret of the origin of life, had to descend to the lowest stages of material, to its most intricate structure into the world of microphysics, the world of molecules and atoms. Here alone, in the recently revealed field of nuclear physics, can we hope to encounter the first traces of life. Here other laws apply than in the purely causal world of macrophysics;

here applies the law of inconceivable potential, the law of statistics or coincidence—whichever we prefer to call it. A gramme of water, for example, contains 100,000 trillion atoms, and similar astronomical figures obtain in the intricate structure of the components of primeval slime, from which presumably life originally sprang.

Countless rudimentary stages of the living substance undoubtedly disappeared because they were not up to standard. The best-suited survived. In other words, in a few of the countless "experimental sites" in the primeval ocean slime groups of atoms combined with molecules containing the material capable of reproduction. As we have said, we can only reconstruct this convincingly in experiments since Nature herself has given us no subsequent object lessons in this field. The primeval cause is clear. If somewhere on the earth today organic substances were to collect, either in the normal or possible way, by "spontaneous generation", they would be destroyed by putrefactive bacteria or other micro-organisms within a very short space of time. But in the springtime of the earth there were as yet no bacteria, and thus in its early stages life had no enemies to threaten its experiments.

What was the next stage in the development? We were not present, and no scientist will ever be in a position to reconstruct the events which occurred over such immeasurable periods of time. This is immaterial, however, for recent experiments have revealed everything that is of basic importance. At some period in the proto-history of the earth, at certain suitable spots, atom groups combined with molecules which could reproduce by auto-catalysis. The best of them became constant. They adapted themselves ever better to the given conditions, increasing to larger constructions, no doubt in a purely casual manner at the outset. This procedure we have also been able to reconstruct in the laboratory, and once more the experiments of Professor Oparin have proved very impressive. In his experiments he found that the protein molecules formed of inorganic material combined with larger structures of a more or less fortuitous character. These structures could absorb certain materials and, as a result, create somewhat complicated chemical "organisations". This is roughly the way in which the chemistry of interest to us here took place on the proto-earth. It is naturally a very long way from these protein droplets to the first single cell, but the principle at least is comprehensible. Moreover, there was time enough for the further development of life and therefore time enough for experimentation.

We can now say without exaggeration that the basic chemical events which ultimately led to the formation of the first living creatures are at least in principle no longer a mystery. The first step consisted in the formation of organic combinations from inorganic material; the second produced the necessary catalysts (enzymes), with the aid of which reproduction of the protein structures was made possible; the third step finally led to the formation of living cells. Billions of years, countless "experimental sites" in the oceans and on their muddy shores . . . then somewhere at a propitious moment the "right" molecules combined to form an organism, naturally a very primitive one. Logically this first primitive living creature could not be an animal because it would immediately have starved; at the time of its creation there were no animals and no plants. The first living organism, therefore, was a plant, presumably a very primitive forerunner of the algæ. With the aid of the energy engendered by solar radiation it could feed itself since, as all plants do today, it transformed this light into chemical energy by photosynthesis. This was in any case only possible if the first algæ had chlorophyll available for the building of their ingestive system.

In order to check the question, American biologists, in very difficult experiments, reconstructed the conditions prevailing on the proto-earth at this particular geological period. Carbon dioxide, ammonia, and water vapour were led over heated silica, which was meant to represent the hot primeval rock. The result was of the greatest interest: an incredibly complicated organic compound (porphyrin), closely related chemically to chlorophyll, was formed. This remarkable experiment proved that a spontaneous, biologically decisive formation of important material (above all, chlorophyll) was possible during the early stages of the earth. It can therefore have formed at various places of its own accord, resulting in organic "raw material" with the aid of which the first vegetable single cells were, so to speak, capable of life. Here was the proto-nourishment upon which subsequently formed animal organisms could live.

Unlimited time, endless possibilities for independent experiment, the most favourable results of which would lead to "products" which could reproduce themselves—this, in certain given conditions, could render possible the beginnings of life. It was certainly no sudden event but the result of interminable instances of trial and error, resulting in many failures and very few successes. But ultimately here and there the most favourable characters accumulated in certain "experimental systems", and the first plant cells were followed by the first animal cells. We cannot of course tell when this actually occurred in time. We can only say that in the course of this stage-by-stage development structures were formed which eventually bore the distinguishing marks of life. Once a start was made, further development is not difficult to foresee. It was merely a question of "organisation", and on this score Nature displays a mastery which never fails to astound anyone actively employed in such fields of research. Finally, the "planned" living creatures had to combine a great variety of characters in order to be able to survive—to mention only a few of the most important, the capacities for growth, irritability, reproduction, nutrition and metabolism, locomotion and defence against enemies. All this developed from the initial stage to that perfected mastery which we meet with in the higher animals. In man, however, the last and highest product of this amazing millennial development on earth, the creation became self-conscious. We know only single details of this process, but the principles of life are now comprehensible and this knowledge can only make us admire and marvel the more at its harmony and plasticity.

CHAPTER III

The Nature of Life

SOMEWHERE in a lonely region stands a house. A curious visitor would like to know more about it, but the whole neighbourhood is out of bounds and everywhere he sees NO TRESPASSING signs. He has no alternative but to confine himself to watching outside events. He sees food and fuel being brought into the house, smoke curling from the chimneys at mealtimes, or perhaps rubbish being carried away, but of what actually goes on inside he can form only a very vague idea. A well-known biologist once compared the living organism to a mystery house of this kind. He meant that we are able to observe the course of all manner of processes in the realm of the living substance, but that, even with the most subtle methods of modern research, we are hard put to it to analyse life itself. We have not as yet fully explored its basic processes and there remain more question marks than certainties on the paths followed in this difficult quest. Modern science cannot even give us the answer to the question: what is the actual nature of life, and in what respect does it differ from lifeless matter? The layman sees this difference quite clearly. Men, animals and plants are "living", whereas the salt on our table is "dead" for it gives no sign of life—this is lifeless matter. But one of the typical marks of life is undoubtedly growth. Take a concentrated solution of salt, and we soon see how the first salt crystals start to grow in the solution, how new crystals join the others—in fact, growth without life!

The same applies, for example, to another feature of the living creature: the capacity to move. As school children we learn of a tiny inhabitant of our ponds, the single-celled amœba. We may have been able to examine these protozoa under the microscope and observe their curious methods of locomotion. They form feet when necessary; they allow these lobate structures to flow ahead in the required direction and can make excellent progress with these pseudopodia. At the end of the 19th cen-

tury, when we still hoped to discover the secret of life by very
simple means, the German biologist Bütschli caused quite a
sensation with his "artificial amœbæ". They were made from
an oil soap compound and not only bore an amazing resemblance to their living model but could actually move with the
aid of pseudopodia. They did this for a whole week although
they were "dead" material. Actually the resemblance was
purely external because they lacked the prerequisites for life
such as food absorption, metabolism, etc. In a modern laboratory it is simple to reproduce all the outward signs of life with
astonishing exactitude. Growth and movement, irritability and
the healing of wounds—all these can be successfully imitated
by the appropriate experiments. But attempts such as these,
which were carried out enthusiastically in the days of Haeckel,
are today of interest only in very special cases. We know that
they represent mere analogies. We could never create true life
in this manner because its working secrets lie hidden at far
deeper levels than could be plumbed by such superficial
imitations.

The earth is peopled with an infinite variety of organisms of
all types. They make love and fight, grow and multiply. They
feel and, in their highest forms, live a conscious life—but in
their construction they all use a minimum of chemical elements.
These are in the main carbon, nitrogen, hydrogen and oxygen.
To these basic materials, with which Nature's laboratory works,
we must add a few more elements, such as iron, magnesium,
phosphorus, calcium and sulphur.

For the greater part of its "output" life uses only three basic
materials: fats, as well as the various forms of sugar, the starches
and the versatile cellulose, etc., consist exclusively of compounds of carbon, hydrogen and oxygen. The most important
as regards life is carbon, which possesses the special ability to
combine in a vast number of ways with other basic materials.
The indisputable progress made by modern chemists working
in this field of carbon compounds, some of which have even
been made synthetically, is far overshadowed by the actual
laboratory of life. Our chemical industries produce with lavish
techniques organic materials such as dyes, artificial rubber,
pharmaceutical products, etc. The living organism, however,
delivers, with the greatest of ease and the minimum of space,

tens—no, hundreds of thousands of chemical compounds. With the few basic materials life requires it builds highly complex organisations of all types. We might almost say that life starts where things become most complicated chemically: this intricacy of building methods is also a peculiarity of the living substance. In the laboratory of life, for example, the material needed for nourishment is chemically worked upon in an uninterrupted flow, is broken down into simple combinations and reformed into complicated components of body substance. As is well known, in the case of the higher animals the food is carried, after its reduction, to every part of the body with the aid of the blood circulation. The body then builds the necessary substances from the red sap, the hæmoglobin. Although we take all this for granted, on closer inspection it is a really amazing feat. How can we explain that bones or nails, muscles or reserve stocks of fat, are built up from the same blood? How is it possible that thousands of chemical processes take place simultaneously, side by side and interdependently, with the end effect that the body is built up and preserved according to a well-conceived plan?

Here we approach the kernel of our problem. In the bodies of the higher animals life rises to an almost inconceivable mastery and variety in the organisation of its substance. No wonder many biologists are of the opinion that all human knowledge ends here and that it is quite pointless to try and get a glimpse into the innermost mysteries. But in the last few decades we have at least succeeded in lifting the veil with which Nature has for so long shrouded these events. Today we know a number of her "building methods" and even if we cannot imitate them successfully we can at least begin to understand them. Firstly, the magnificent achievements of life, as opposed to the behaviour of inorganic substances, are bound by seemingly clear-cut conditions: only with given temperatures, conditions of light, and the presence of air and water can higher organisms thrive. These are the prerequisites for life we have already mentioned. A few exceptions seem to flout these normally indispensable conditions: certain algæ can live in hot water up to 176° F and some micro-organisms can endure degrees of cold approaching absolute zero, but these exceptions apply only to lower stages in evolution. The more highly

organised creatures, as a result of their more complex constructions, are very sensitive to any deviation from their norm.
Should the climate, for example, become too hot or too cold, or
the moisture inadequate, higher life succumbs to such changes
in their natural conditions to the point of extinction.

Nature in her physical building methods makes the widest
possible use of a fact long since known to chemists: that chemical changes of any kind occur best in liquid. As we know, man
is to a large extent composed of water. An embryo in the third
month is 90% water; we "dry out" a little later, but in the
adult body the tissues, etc., consist of between 70% and 75%
water. It must not be supposed that all materials will be subject to reaction merely by being dissolved in the appropriate
masses of water in the organism. The chemist works with his
acids, salts, etc., in test-tubes and retorts, and many of the substances react when dissolved in brine, but the organism has
other methods. Its cells contain no solution in the ordinary
sense of the word, but a very special distributive form which
has only recently been studied—the so-called colloidal sol-
vents. When we put a lump of sugar in our morning coffee the
sugar melts completely in a very short time; the sugar is dissolved, which means that its molecules disintegrate to a liquid
invisible to our eyes or a microscope.

The antithesis to such a "true solution", as chemists call it,
can be observed when, as a remedy against stomach trouble,
we concoct a blackish brew by dissolving a tablet of charcoal in
water. In this case the tablet disappears but it does not dis-
solve: it is dispersed roughly throughout the water. This is
known as suspension, and clay in the dirty water of a river
affords another example. Between this state and "true solution" stand the colloids. They possess, so to speak, ideal qualities for fulfilling the infinite variety of demands made on the
living substance. Thanks to the fine distribution of the material
in such a solution, its surface on the one hand is enlarged a
million times compared with the solid state, while on the other
hand it retains certain functions essential to life which would be
lost in true solution. Furthermore, colloidal solutions are of an
almost mimosa-like sensitivity and react swiftly and intensely
to the slightest change, such as degrees of acidity, salt content,
etc. It holds good, above all, for the frequent changes in the

body between "solid" and "liquid". This condition of "eternal flux" of metabolism is characteristic of many life processes. Here, once more, we are faced with a very important difference from the much more rigid processes in organic material.

THE "METHODOLOGY" OF LIFE

According to an excellent definition by the well-known biologist Professor Muller, the characteristic feature of life consists in its capacity to organise materials in a prescribed manner. Therein lies its difference from the inanimate world. Let us take as our example those constructions which stand on the bottom rung of the evolutionary ladder and which may appear in crystalline form—the viruses to which we have already referred. The largest species, which include the small-pox–psittacosis group, conform by and large to the format of the smallest bacteria. At the other end of the scale we have such viruses as the provocative agent of foot and mouth disease, measuring in the neighbourhood of 8 to 12 milli-microns—i.e. approaching molecular dimensions. The American biochemist W. M. Stanley was the first to succeed in proving, in the case of a certain virus, that it was actually nothing but a molecule and, to be more precise, a protein molecule. The example studied by Stanley was the tobacco mosaic virus, the redoubtable enemy of the tobacco grower. An infinitesimal number of these can induce necrosis in the tobacco plant, which can destroy vast plantations within a short space of time. This virus, abhorred by all lovers of the "noble weed", held a great surprise in store for biology. In its pure form it will crystallise. These crystals behave not one whit differently from any other organic material such as hæmoglobin. No one will seriously maintain that a quantity of hæmoglobin in the laboratory is "alive". It is "dead" material, like sugar or salt, even though it originated from a living organism. The crystals of the tobacco mosaic virus can be preserved for long periods and they look as harmless as any other crystal, but place them on a tobacco leaf and the "dead" material immediately comes to life again—very intensely, and to the detriment of countless tobacco plants unless great caution is observed in the experiment.

In 1955 Stanley's colleagues succeeded in taking another

step forward. By chemical means they broke up the substance of the "living" tobacco mosaic virus into its main components, protein and nucleic acid. Both were subjected to countless tests, which proved that they were dealing with entirely dead material; but this dead material was now reconstituted by complicated chemical processes, and behold: it was suddenly alive once more! Perfectly formed viruses were obtained. These proceeded to reproduce on tobacco leaves and to induce the typical signs of the tobacco plant necrosis.

We can at least give a fundamental explanation of this very remarkable event, and it affords us an insight into the methodology of life. Viruses are, so to speak, incomplete living organisms, lacking important features of the normal organism; but in the cells of their "hosts" they are able to metamorphose from apparently dead to living material. It is possible because, under the conditions prevailing in the foreign cell, the parasites now have the capacity to reproduce. Dr. J. Hausen points out in his book *Stars, Genes and Mesons* that viruses in themselves represent isolated cell structures. As such they are lifeless and only start to live in the true sense of the word when they invade the foreign cell.

A typical though uncongenial fact emerges: living matter is so organised that the existence of any living type, once established, is assured. This holds good equally for viruses, bacteria, animals or man; it holds good for the organism as a whole as well as for its parts. The organs are built of suitably organised tissue, the latter of cells, and these in turn, of the respective best-suited components of the most varied nature. The "building bricks" are the so-called macromolecules, which we must examine a little more closely because, without a knowledge of them, the nature of life remains incomprehensible. The actual living substance is, as we know, protein and its essential features are determined by the fact that it has the special capacity for forming macromolecules. This new and in many respects very important trend in research was introduced by the German biologist, Professor Staudinger, who was awarded the Nobel Prize for his discoveries.

MACROMOLECULES AS THE BUILDING MATERIAL OF THE LIVING SUBSTANCE

Throughout our lives the cells of our bodies are in a constant process of renewal. Without a pause, digestion, the building of new cells and all the complex processes of life, which even the best biochemist cannot reproduce, continue to function. Biologists have long been in search of the appropriate "living units" capable of such achievement, of the building-blocks of the organism which to a certain extent serve as a link between the "ordinary" molecules and the much larger building material of the cells. This link was found in the macromolecules. While very few atoms go to form the molecules of water or cooking salt, protein is formed of molecules, each containing millions of atoms. On account of the peculiarities of its macromolecular constitution, a protein, for example, can assume so many different forms that their number exceeds all the drops of water in all the oceans of the world. In support of this astounding statement let us quote the words of Professor Staudinger himself:

"An endless number of proteins, which differ from each other chemically and physically, is possible. The possibility thus arises that every living organism, whether of the present or from earlier periods of the history of the earth, has its own protein molecule. This deduction is basically comprehensible, for in the last analysis the chemical accomplishments of each living organism must differ from each other. From a given germ a certain prescribed individual will be born time after time similar to, but not identical with, its peers. It is the existence of the macromolecules that makes possible the fantastic variants in the materials used in the life process."

This statement is fully justified, for it would be hard to conceive of anything more complicated or varied than the "building-blocks" with which life works. The most important of these are the proteins. Their attributes exceed in complexity everything with which, for our sins, we biochemists have to work. Proteins in fact form the decisive building materials for the actual living substance—protoplasm. No one can determine the exact number of proteins that exist for they are incalculable. We can say without exaggeration that almost any single molecule of any given protein is an individual, that its composition is rarely repeated and that it is very often unique.

Now to compare a protein molecule, as a component of the living substance, to the molecule of some inorganic material is rather like comparing a mountain with a pebble. Let us take our old example the tobacco mosaic virus. Its molecular weight has recently been assessed at 17 million, whereas that of water is merely 18 million! This is by no means a record, for the molecular weight of another virus (causing a certain skin disease in rabbits) is 25 million. Admittedly we are dealing here with macromolecules of an exceedingly complicated structure, but even the simpler proteins have a high molecular weight and, in comparison with all other outward forms of material, are very complex in construction. In the extraordinary many-sidedness of proteins which, we might say, ensures to every living creature a personal protoplasm, we find an initial explanation for the multiformity of organisms. Without the metabolic possibilities of the protein it would not be possible. Moreover, we also understand now why protoplasm represents a colloidal solution: the protein molecules of which it largely consists are too big to achieve a true solution in water. Colloidal solution alone makes possible such an internal, variable and protean relation to water as we find in the living substance.

Intrinsically the inner nature of protoplasm and its proteins, even in modern research, poses the same difficult problems as before. We know that all proteins are built of smaller molecules (biochemists call them amino-acids) and that they undergo *inter se* and with other material countless associations and combinations. Protoplasm results from a wealth of the most disparate proteins of this type. We cannot blame the biochemist for not having yet clarified the question of the chemical constitution of this actual bearer of life. It is hard to realise that the same applies not only to its chemical structure, which changes from case to case: its physical phenomena are also very varied, ranging from thin liquid to solid, and with constant interchange between these two stages of gel and sol. Even in the realm of the minutest protozoa protoplasm displays its physical metabolic arts. The beautiful heliozoan or sun animalcule of our

ponds, for example, reveals, under the microscope, flagella surrounding tiny molecules of the single cell like an aura. In these
flagella the liquid protoplasm is firm, but at a touch they can
liquify once more; the "solid" rays form and disappear at will.

THE CELL AS BUILDING MATERIAL

If such transformations occur among the most primitive
forms of life, then we should not be surprised that the chemical
and physical jugglery of protoplasm in the bodies of metazoa
and plants should achieve further triumphs. Here, as opposed
to the amœbæ, the substance of life is not distributed uniformly
throughout the entire organism but assumes every conceivable
form in the various cells and cell groups in a constant process of
metabolism. The body of an adult man consists of billions of
such cells; it is common knowledge how many different types
of cells there are. They are all aggregates of proteins of varying
composition, surrounding the differently built-up nuclei. The
cells enjoy a comparatively wide independence, and this is why
they were once called "elementary organisms". If we remove
certain cell groups—e.g. gland, muscle, skin, or even nerve cells
that build up the brain (neurons)—with the utmost care from
their seat in the body, they can in the truest sense of the word
become independent. We have only to provide them with a
suitable soil on which to feed and such cells will continue to live
outside the body, in some cases for many years.

A famous experiment in this field was made by Alexis Carrel
at the Rockefeller Institute. He removed a few cells from the
heart of a freshly killed chicken and placed them in a suitable
alimentary liquid. They continued to grow and reproduce
until, from time to time, "superfluous" tissue had to be removed. These cells lived for 34 years in the container. They
did not die, but the experiment was broken off, having duly
served its purpose. Similar tests have been made with all types
of cell and the results were invariably the same: the cells can
live and reproduce equally well in the laboratory as in the body
itself by reason of their remarkable independence. Even the
most primitive cells have a greater capacity than the most intricate piece of machinery. No one can envisage a self-winding
watch that repairs itself and multiplies. The body can do this
and a lot more besides.

Then there are the so-called "organisers", whose discovery won the Nobel Prize for the German biologist, Spemann. He removed two small pieces of tissue from two salamander embryos at a very early stage of development—the first piece from the region of the future belly skin of one, and the second from the future brain of the other. These two morsels of tissue destined to such very different purposes he now grafted on to the two embryos; but he exchanged them, placing a piece of belly skin in the region of the future brain, and vice versa. What was the result? Both parts thrived and developed in the "wrong places"—exactly like "correct" tissue—in their new surroundings: the piece destined to become belly skin became brain, and the future brain became belly skin. However, when the experiment was repeated with portions of tissue from a more developed embryo they no longer adapted themselves to their new surroundings but developed according to Nature's original plan. Spemann was also able to graft tissue from an embryo frog on to a salamander embryo. In this case the foreign tissue, inserted in the region of the mouth, developed as part of the mouth. But once more the tissue, removed at a late stage, did not become the mouth of a salamander but the mouth of a frog, in accordance with the origin of the cells. By these experiments Spemann demonstrated that a certain part of the germ cell has the capacity to organise the eventual physical form, hence the name "organiser" given to this most remarkable contrivance of life.

It was later discovered that the growing embryo was influenced by chemical materials from its environment and that the most varied influences, such as heat, pressure, etc., could bring about similar changes in development. In the initial stages of its development the embryo creates new "regulating materials", which act as form organisers. This is how enzymes, which affect the chemistry of growth, are formed. At certain stages of embryonic development protein molecules not formerly present, hormones, step in and take control.

As development proceeds the cells of the embryo specialise more and more; tissue and organs form and the structure of the organism becomes increasingly complicated—and yet all this proceeds according to the "inner goal" directed at the formation of the ultimate living creature. The organisation of this development obviously follows by stages, the regulating centres "instructing" the cells to a certain degree how they are to behave in future. But matters here can be compared with the rehearsal of a new play. The best director can only achieve his purpose if the actors are capable of following his instructions. The regulating centres of the embryo can only solve events of growth which the cells already "know". They possess a scheme of reactions and this, by changes of the normal events— e.g. in experiment—will cause reactions in the original building plan. It is not true to say that all future forms are latent in the ova. It would be more correct to say that the development of the embryo proceeds in a hierarchically built sequence of ever higher formations. Each of them has functional specialities to fulfil and, in turn, calls forth further new building achievements.

An extraordinary capacity for adaptation is shown by certain animals in the matter of regeneration—i.e. the power of the mature individual to replace lost portions of the body. In favourable conditions the fresh water polyp, for example, can perform the miracle of growing a complete new body from only a two-hundredth of its bodily mass. The talents of earthworms in this respect are well-known. The higher we climb on the evolutionary ladder the less becomes the power to regenerate. In principle such "renewal" of body tissue follows the same scheme as in the development of the embryo: undifferentiated embryonic cells appear, divide, and finally replace the missing parts. The higher vertebrates and man cannot replace lost limbs as batrachians and fish can do: our highly specialised bodies can merely heal wounds, no more.

"MANUFACTURING METHODS" IN THE CELL CITY

When we examine a cell under the microscope we see within it the clearly defined nucleus surrounded by a jelly-like substance, the cytoplasm. The nucleus determines the structure and sees to it that, on the building of new cells by division, the "right" building-blocks of the organism are produced. Thus lung cells produce only lung cells, epithelial cells produce only skin cells, etc. In this way it comes about that in the constant change of substance the form remains stable. The time taken in building new cells is very varied and conforms in general to the need in question. If, for example, one is very energetic, the muscle substance will increase substantially and the heart will adapt itself in an astonishing manner to the increased demands made upon it. In a healthy man it weighs about 10 oz., but under great stress—for instance, in cases of blood pressure—it can attain a weight of between 18 and 21 oz. by increase of the working cell substance. If a diseased kidney is removed, the cell growth in the remaining kidney increases because it now has to do the work of two. Conversely, too little use of muscle and bone causes such considerable reduction in the building of new cells that atrophy ensues. When someone breaks a leg skiing and the leg has to remain for a long time in plaster, it takes a long time before the muscle starts to function normally again once the plaster is removed. The structure and function of the cells are therefore closely connected.

A well-known biologist summed up the activities of the cell with the following analogy: "When we consider the teeming activity of a modern city it is difficult to realise that in the cells of our bodies infinitely more complicated processes are at work—ceaseless manufacture, acquisition of food, storage, improvement, transport, disposal of waste, surveillance, communication and administration." All this takes place in superb harmony, with the co-operation of all the participants of a living system, regulated down to the smallest detail. Each distributive process is so controlled that it only runs for so long and within such bounds as best serve the interests of the whole body. The cells of the pancreas produce just the right amount of insulin to keep the sugar content in the remaining cells functioning properly. Fat cells store up reserve material for emergencies, digestive cells generate the ferments needed for digestion, cell reproduction is regulated with precision, etc. To take the last-mentioned as an illustration, we know only too well what happens when the regulation of cell reproduction breaks down. Certain cells begin to grow in an undisciplined manner, increasing to excess and thereby causing grievous damage to the organism. We speak then of cancer, and despite our untiring efforts we have not yet been able to solve the faulty regulation of the growth of certain cells.

But there are unsolved problems enough in cytology, the study of cells. Ever since their branch of science has been in existence physiologists have made an exhaustive study of muscle, examining its functions and chemistry with ever improved methods, and we shall deal later with some of the results, but despite a modicum of success the investigators have been faced with a host of unsolved riddles. A famous specialist in this discipline, Professor Szent György, recently expressed this very sarcastically. "The more data we collect regarding muscle the less we understand its functions. It often seems that we have learned all there is to know about it, but the main characteristic of muscle resides in the fact that we understand nothing of it."

This is perhaps an exaggeration, but fundamentally we find similar problems not only in the case of muscle but in the case of all cells. We know their manifold individual structures (some of them only became visible with the invention of the electron microscope), but it is exceedingly difficult to explore the actual mode of working of this living system. Its chemical components are so numerous that a list of them would fill a whole page. The intricately constructed cytoplasm, the fat-like substances, the carbohydrates, etc., amalgamate once more as macromolecules. Further, the cell contains micro-organs such as the mitochondria, which contain innumerable ferments. They for their part regulate certain chemical events, for instance cell respiration. Of other recently recorded cell structures we only know of their existence but so far have no idea of their actual significance.

The inner structure of living cells changes constantly. An inconceivable number of reactions take place in the building up and breaking down of a host of substances simultaneously and consecutively. The cell has been defined as a construction in a constant state of transformation, and no stable framework actually exists. According to the German cytologist, Professor Burgmann, the structure in the cell itself is in flux. The function of the whole cell depends on the totality of the consummating flux of the structural changes. In other words, the normal condition of a cell, as of the whole organism, can be maintained only by a wealth of physico-chemical events, and this is the decisive peculiarity of life.

Viewed from this standpoint, the long and bitter controversy that raged between the "mechanistic" and "vitalistic" interpretations of the phenomena of life had become outdated. At the outset the mechanistic school maintained that all the events of life could be traced back to the physico-chemical laws that apply to inanimate Nature. We have already referred to the over-optimistic theories of the biologists of about 1900, who tried in their laboratories to solve all the universal riddles from "spontaneous generation" to the human soul, and who even hoped to create life artificially. This conception of the world collapsed, since when we have grown more modest and sober. Today we view all "patent solutions" in this field with justifiable scepticism, from whichever side they may come. The earlier mechanistic theory, which saw the living creature as nothing but "agitated matter" and explained thoughts as "secretions of the brain", was just such a patent solution. Its refutation was largely due to the vitalists, who pointed out time and time again the fundamental differences between the living and the inanimate. Above all, they drew the attention of biologists to a fact which today is recognised in both camps as being of paramount importance—an understanding of vitality: the total application of life. An organism is more than the sum of its individual parts. All the complicated processes in the cells, the functions of the organs, etc., invariably follow in the service of the superior "totalities" of the individual and ultimately of the species.

But vitalism in its latest form, as expounded by Hans Driesch, fundamentally rejects the recognition of the nature of life by natural scientific methods. He postulates a metaphysical principle which, borrowing an Aristotelian term, he calls entelechy and considers different in its nature from all material. It is not within the scope of this book to enter into these philosophical problems too closely. Furthermore, the development of modern biology has led to explanations which are neither mechanistic nor vitalistic, but correspond to our knowledge of life in every respect. The latter has become intelligible in the scientific sense, now that we have recognised and studied more closely the particular organisation of the living substance in the shape of macromolecules. We still know virtually nothing of countless details of the life processes but, at least basically, the way to their elucidation lies open.

THE SOURCE OF LIFE

Everything living is engaged in a mighty field of tension which, for millions of years, has never for a moment lost its power. This is the tension between the sensitivity of organisms to all external and internal influences; their lability and transitoriness on the one hand, and the urge towards eternity and survival on the other. We shall deal with the question of the human life-span in a later chapter. Of far greater importance is the solution taken by Nature for the preservation of life in all individual living creatures, the solution whereby time is conquered—i.e. the renewal of individuals. In order to achieve this goal the creative ingenuity of Nature drew upon an inexhaustible fund of methods. Special safeguards were devised above all to ensure, by reproduction and propagation, a surplus of progeny beyond the actual needs. In lower life there are many known forms which in no way conform to the concept of individuality considered so important by humans: they simply divide, and their whole reproductory process consists in one cell becoming two. At the second division these two become four, and by the fourteenth division the figure reaches 16,384 entities. Now since certain organisms, for example bacteria, can divide every half-hour, there is no chance of there being a shortage; in fact, there would be a danger of the earth being inundated by them had not effective brakes in the shape of food shortage and other factors been devised to prevent unrestricted production. Nature sees to it that a certain balance is preserved between "production" and "destruction" rates, so that the total of individuals remains more or less constant.

But life as such has an urge towards immortality, towards overcoming time, and realises this with a great variety of methods. So various are they in fact that it has taken biologists a long time to obtain even an overall glimpse of them, and in this field there are still a host of questions that remain unanswered. Just over a hundred years ago the Austrian botanist Franz Unger discovered that algæ behaved very strangely during reproduction. Examining confervæ under the microscope, he observed that from time to time one of the filaments cut itself adrift from the others, burst open its utricle, and suddenly, before his eyes, a dark green infusorial globule swam away, motivated by countless cilia. From a plant, therefore, had been born an infusorial cell which after a time started to behave like an animal, only to attach itself once more and grow as a confervum. In his enthusiasm Unger wrote a book entitled *The Plant at the Moment of Becoming an Animal*, accurately describing his observations, even though his explanation turned out to be partly false. Today we know that several primitive plants reproduce in the manner of algæ: they form mobile cells known as zoospores. In the case of water plants these reproductive cells acquire in the process a kind of oar in the form of flagella. Land plants on the contrary merely entrust these spores to the air. The brown dust which rises like smoke when we squeeze potato mould, or the yellow powder of the lycopodium, which children use as make-believe "lightning" by blowing it through a flame, are merely vast quantities of reproductive cells.

In the case of the higher plants the methods of reproduction are rather more complicated. To begin with, there are the multicellular reproductive cells, located in the case of the Liliaceæ as bulbils, or offset buds, in the leaf axils.

These finally fall off and grow into new plants. Other plant organs, however, can form rhizomes or roots which, when parted from the mother plant, will grow into a new individual. Horticulturists exploit this type of reproduction with their cuttings: it is known as vegetative reproduction, and a similar form is found among lower forms of life. Growth and vegetative production are so closely interwoven in some plants that it is often difficult to see where the old individual ceases and the new one begins. A typical example is the banyan or Indian fig. Its seed first sprouts on other plants, to which it is carried by birds. After a time the roots begin to entwine the trunk of its "host", which is eventually strangled completely. In the meantime they reach the ground, where they absorb food and water, thicken, and finally become a new trunk of the banyan. From each branch new roots grow down to the ground, and from each of these is born another tree trunk, until at last from a single seed a single banyan can form a whole forest with a dense network of trunks and branches. Anyone observing a banyan would be hard put to it to decide whether he were looking at an individual or a number of trees.

A GLIMPSE INTO THE WORKSHOP OF LIFE

The case of the banyan is only one impressive example of a constantly recurring fact—that the two biological events, growth and reproduction, are interchangeable in the abstract sense. There is a very simple reason for this: both go back to the same cause, to *cell division*. At the outset a cluster of filaments, consisting of a special strongly colorific mass called chromatin (Greek: *chroma* = colour) forms in the nucleus. The cluster disintegrates into a host of single strands known as chromosomes (which have become one of the most vital objects for scientific research in modern biology). They appear in each dividing cell in a specific number for each individual animal or plant. Their number can vary between 2 and 200, but the manner of partition of chromosomes is invariable throughout the whole realm of life, allowing us to suspect the deep meaning that lies beneath this extraordinarily complicated occurrence.

When the chromosomes form and arrange themselves in a star-shaped pattern—the nuclear membrane has in the meantime disappeared—they begin to divide, oddly enough longitudinally. During this another event takes place in the cell: a structure is formed, known from its shape as the spindle. Each strand of this spindle attaches itself to one chromatid or halved length of a dividing chromosome; it contracts laterally and in this way draws the chromatid to one pole of the cell. Similarly the second chromatid reaches the other pole, and now each half of the cell contains the same number of halved chromosomes. This stage having been reached, a further cluster forms from the two chromosome groups and two new nuclei develop. Now the protoplasm of the original cell also divides, forming transverse walls. The mother cell has divided into two daughter cells. This procedure occurs in the cells of all living creatures with the exception of a few single-celled types. Each growth of the organism follows in the same way, and these remarkable events are the determining factors in the formation of new individuals through reproduction.

In the old days people spoke of vegetative or asexual reproduction, which we meet with, above all, in plants and the lower forms of animal life, but among all higher forms procreation is bound up with the two sexes. But why is this so? The question might appear superfluous, for we find it only natural that in Nature there should be male and female combining to produce offspring. As we have already observed on several occasions, it is a mistake to take things for granted in Nature, and sometimes the simplest questions are the hardest to answer. This is a case in point. For thousands of years men have asked the question from every conceivable angle as to how the polarity of male and female arose. More than four hundred theories have been advanced, but none of them, alas, has provided an empirical solution.

We know that in sexual procreation a fusion of the male and female germ cells results. This was a very late discovery, when considering the length of time man has wracked his brains over the biological foundations of his existence. Not until 1875 did O. Hertwig recognise the nature of fecundation as the union of ovum and spermatozoon, and then only from a specially favourable object for experiment—the egg of a sea-urchin. Whereas in a mammal fecundation takes place deep inside the body, things are far simpler in the case of the sea-urchin. This small marine animal releases ova and spermatozoa in the water, where fecundation ensues. We can experiment with these germ cells today, as chemists do, by uniting the two substances in a test tube. Another great advantage is the fact that sea-urchin eggs are crystal clear, which aids observation considerably. Hertwig was the first to observe that the spermatozoa penetrate the ova after the loss of their tails. They travel to the nucleus and blend with it. Since the main mass of the spermatozoon consists of nucleic substance, the nature of the event of fecundation turned out to be the fusion of two nuclei. Cell division is induced, and the development of the new protoplasm can now begin. In order to reach this goal, Nature employs a whole bag of tricks devised solely to bring the two sexes together. In the lower forms of life this follows in a comparatively simple manner, while in the case of the higher animals the whole gamut of instincts is brought into play and in man we have to take Eros and the psyche into account.

STRANGE METHODS OF FECUNDATION

Life does not care for the stereotyped and takes many paths towards its goal. This applies equally to fecundation. The method of the sea-urchin of entrusting the male and female germ cells to the water is followed by the majority of fish. Several species are known to collect in big shoals during the spawning season. This affords a chance of the greatest possible number of eggs being fertilised. We meet with the most remarkable conditions among deep sea fish, which live in complete darkness. So that the sexes can find each other, they carry lanterns on their bodies—as glow-worms do—lanterns of great variety regarding arrangement, luminosity and number, whereby each species can be recognised. It was found that many fish living in these deep waters swim around with "pendants", which scientists at first mistook for young. Since this seemed rather unusual, Professor T. Rogan studied these alleged young and found that they had neither mouths nor intestines of their own and, in fact, lived entirely as parasites. He finally discovered the answer to the problem. The pendants were not young but males—very small and very dependent males, for they lived at the expense of the females! In this way fertilisation of the eggs was ensured. The dwarfs have no other task than to generate spermatozoa and are, we might say, a peculiar type of degenerate germ cell carried about permanently by the females.

The fecundation methods of some spiders are very strange. The male spins a small web, on which it leaves a little seminal fluid. Next it introduces the drops into a kind of pouch situated at the end of the maxillary palps on its head. The pouch has a minute aperture from which the male can then squirt sperm into the female's vulva. Such remarkable variations are all part of Nature's repertoire in the service of reproduction and the preservation of the species. Countless methods of attraction serve the same purpose, namely to allow the sexes to find each other. From the marriage garb of the stickleback and the superb peacock's train to the love dances of many animals (and primitives!) runs a single line, showing how Nature uses a host of possibilities hardly to be found in any other field of her activities.

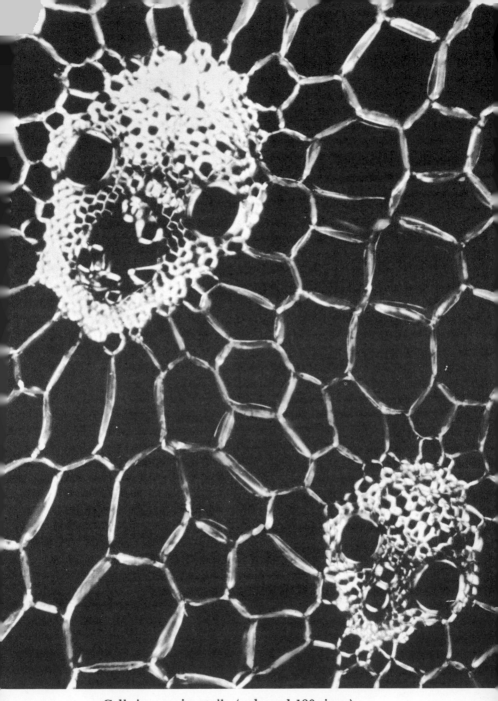

Cells in a maize stalk (enlarged 180 times).

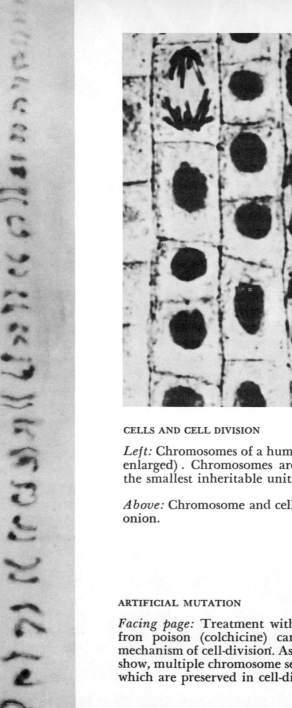

CELLS AND CELL DIVISION

Left: Chromosomes of a human cell (greatly enlarged) . Chromosomes are formed from the smallest inheritable units, the genes.

Above: Chromosome and cell division of an onion.

ARTIFICIAL MUTATION

Facing page: Treatment with meadow saffron poison (colchicine) can change the mechanism of cell-division. As these pictures show, multiple chromosome sets are formed, which are preserved in cell-division.

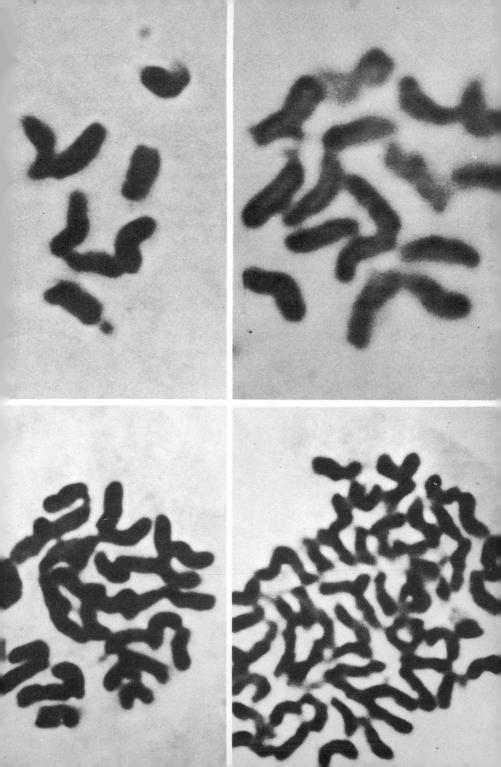

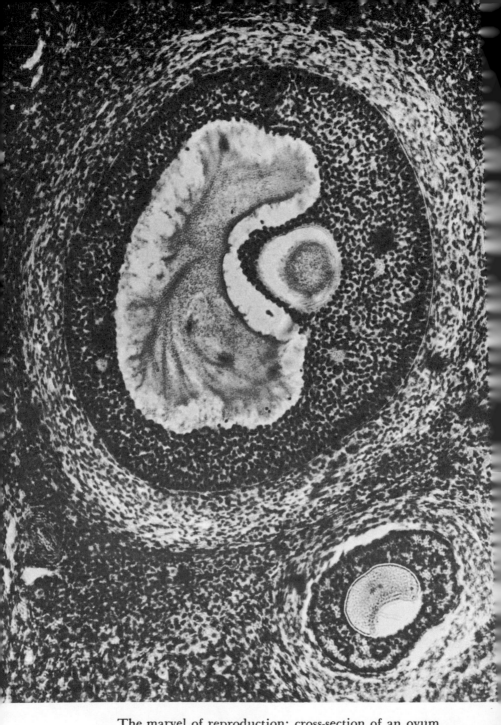

The marvel of reproduction: cross-section of an ovum.

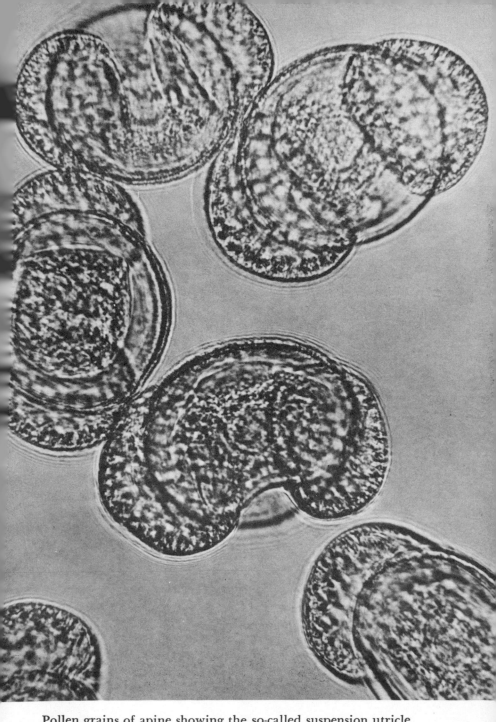

Pollen grains of apine showing the so-called suspension utricle (enlarged 1,000 times).

STRANGE EGGS

Nature, in the reproduction of the species, employs an endless variety of methods and forms.

Above: Cockroach (egg cocoons).

Below: Stick insect.

Catfish. *(Triacis semifasciatus.)*

Cabbage white butterfly. *(Pieris rapae.)*

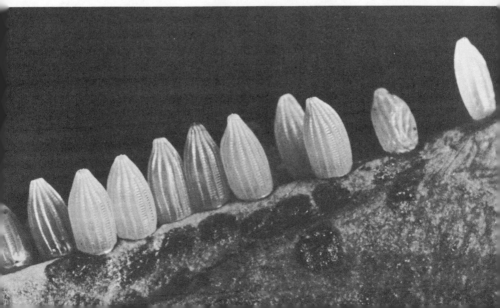

Annulary caterpillar *(Gastropacha neustria)*, a small butterfly.

This holds good for plants as well as animals. The erroneous idea that we have known about the sexual reproduction of plants only for two to three hundred years has been fostered by text-book after text-book. Of course, sexuality is not nearly so apparent in plants as in animals, and in addition most of the former are hermaphroditic, incorporating the male and female sexual organs in one flower. The ancient Egyptians, however, in the case of two plants of vital importance to them—the fig and the date palm—knew that two sexes were necessary for seeding. In their cultivation of these two plants they used expert artificial pollination. Later, the Roman naturalist Pliny the Elder studied this question, and for the sake of interest we quote his exposition on the date palm:

"It is generally accepted that the female trees in a wild forest cannot bear fruit without a male, and that each male is surrounded by many females who bend their branches down lovingly towards him. The male raises himself stiff and erect, fertilising the females by his scent or gaze or by the pollen he wafts towards them. Should there be no male tree the females stand there widowed and barren, so strong is the sense of love in these trees."

This passage of natural history remained forgotten throughout the Middle Ages, which knew nothing of the subject, and not until the Renaissance was the wisdom of the Ancient Egyptians and of Pliny rediscovered. Prior to this, the question whether plants were subject to the polarity of male and female was either never asked or stoutly denied. At the end of the 17th Century the Tübingen professor, R. J. Camerarius, from experiments with maize, castor oil plants, mulberry trees, etc., confirmed that these plants remained barren if the stamens were removed from their blossoms. A lively polemic ensued, but ultimately it could not be denied that Camerarius was right in attributing sexuality to plants. He had been mistaken on only one point—the belief that in general the blossom is fertilised by its own pollen.

FLORAL WONDERS IN PROSE

G. Koelreuter (1733–1806) had shown that in many plants the pollen is not suitable for fertilisation and that, as a general rule, egg cells and pollen grains must originate from different individuals. In 1793, however, the Berlin botanist K. Sprengel published a book which at one blow solved the mystery of the blossom. This work, with the long-winded title *The newly discovered secret of Nature with regard to the construction and fertilisation of flowers*, provided the bases of "plant biology", a theoretical and unusually important science embracing both zoology and botany. Sprengel had observed how bees, wasps and bumblebees carry the pollen dust from flower to flower, and this led him to the right conclusion that insects serve as messengers of love for many plants. It had previously been taken for granted that the beauty and scent of flowers were designed solely to bring pleasure to man. This proved to be wrong, for in actual fact the most beautiful forms and scents of our flowers have a very specific purpose—to attract the insects which are necessary for pollination and the preservation of the species. The nectar is the tribute paid by the flowers to the insects for this love service. Nevertheless, as in the life of humans, there is no lack of cases where one or another of the partners resorts to malpractice. It has often been observed that bumblebees, instead of using the prescribed entrance to the blossom, prefer to fetch the desirable drops of sweetness by the direct route: they merely bore a hole in the flower, and in this way the plant "customer" is robbed of the pollination.

In other cases the insects are the "stooges" in the truest sense of the word. To many types of plants it is a matter of indifference which insects carry out the pollination, while others are specialised for a particular species, and the traits of the flower often reveal the nature of the invited guest. In the tropics of East Asia, for example, there are several varieties of aristolochia whose giant blooms give off a real stench of carrion, which, in conjunction with the flesh-pink colour, attracts blow flies. The latter topple over the rim of the blossom into a cauldron-like calyx which is covered with thick hair. These hairs all grow in one direction, cannot be bent back, and force the insect to take a particular route into the flower. A faint light falls through a thin section of the petal and arouses false hope in the insect that it can escape through the window. But the exit is closed. At the rim, on the other hand, are the pistils, and their pollen powders the insect in its effort to escape. Once this has happened, a curious metamorphosis takes place inside the flower: the cilia dry out and the escape route is open.

Nature is sprinkled with every conceivable kind of pollen every spring. From a million grains of pollen perhaps a single one fulfils its true purpose. The others die, but not all of them. Some fall to the ground, where the decay of organic substances travels its slow course. This applies in particular to moorland, where the high content of humus acid encourages the activities of bacteria.

It appears to be part and parcel of Nature that nearly every law discovered at the cost of great effort by research should be fraught with exceptions. This particularly applies to all the processes concerning the source of life, and its food problems, preservation, and continuity in successive generations. Each law we are able to confirm contradicts itself at some point, for there exist not only sexual and asexual reproduction but every intermediate and transitional stage between the two. Even our clear-cut conception of sex turns out to be uncertain and equivocal, for Nature thinks nothing of creating living creatures that change their sex and, in some cases, can do so several times in succession.

Let us try to follow life along these tangled paths and begin our quest once more in the labyrinth of sex with the most primitive forms, the protozoa. A few groups of these lowest forms of life are completely sexless, particularly bacteria and the blue-green algæ. All other single-celled creatures normally reproduce by asexual division. Let us then examine under the microscope another exception to this apparent rule. Two of these diminutive creatures approach each other, swim for a while joined together in the water, and ultimately coalesce. These two cells—known as gametes—can resemble each other perfectly to outward appearance, but they can also look dissimilar. In any case, they have "male" and "female" tendencies, thus revealing the principle of sexual differentiation at a level of life where no other differentiation can be maintained. The product of this coalescing, the so-called zygote, is usually resistant to unfavourable influences of the outside world, such as drought and high temperatures. It remains quiet for some time and then delivers motile single-celled offspring, which proceed to reproduce normally by division. From time to time

Nature therefore alternates sexual with asexual reproduction, whereby a remarkable fact emerges: the two coalescing cells, the gametes, can now behave either as "male" or "female". If the gametes are brought in contact with closely related species of algæ, some of them settle and the female cells allow themselves to be embraced by the male cells. Should the female gametes, however, be brought in contact with another type of algæ, they become male, do not settle, but for their part embrace the settled cells of the new algæ.

The method of "sex-change" is to be found among many hermaphroditic animals such as worms, snails and mussels. Like all true hermaphrodites, they possess both male and female germ glands, which they allow to mature in succession. These strange creatures appear first as a male and subsequently as a female, or vice versa. Usually, but not always, the animal remains unchanged in shape. Many mussels and snails undergo a complete metamorphosis of their whole internal and external physical structure. This metamorphosis is so perfect that for a long time zoologists were deceived and mistook these androgynous forms for males and females respectively.

Observations of this nature have given us vital biological information. Fundamentally both sex principles are present in plants, animals and man. Whichever breaks through is decided either by external influences or by hereditary factors. If, for example, in the case of the above-mentioned protozoa, the advantage of the male principle over the female is slight, then weak male cells are produced. They can, for their part, behave as female cells if they happen to encounter strong male cells. This throws some light on a wealth of biological phenomena which was formerly a complete mystery. It is not only plants that are hermaphroditic, in that they possess both male and female organs in their blossoms: all animals are potentially bisexual. The development of a *single* sex is caused by the hormones produced by the germ glands. That man is no exception to this rule is proved by the various intermediate sexual forms to be found both on the physical and intellectual plane.

In other cases Nature shows that she can dispense entirely, or at any rate partially, with the male. In so-called parthenogenesis the ova need no fertilisation but develop unaided. This applies to several insects, such as aphids, worms and water fleas, the favourite fodder of the fish in our aquariums. In the ovaries of these animals eggs develop which do not need to be, and often cannot be, impregnated because male water fleas are rare. But they do not seem to be entirely superfluous because at certain times females will produce two batches of eggs, one of which will develop as usual into females while a brood of males will hatch from the second. The eggs of the next generation can now be fertilised, and since these eggs are resistant to extreme cold they are called winter eggs. How often in the parthenogenetic sequence males will occur, whether once or more times a year, depends largely on climatic factors.

The interesting problem is why Nature, despite so many possibilities for asexual reproduction, has, in the course of evolution, developed to an increasing extent the far more complicated differentiation of organisms into two sexes. The grounds for this probably lie in the fact that in this way a far better combination potential for inherited characters results. Asexual reproduction is very poor in the "production" of new types. Had such a method predominated in the evolutionary scale, life on earth would probably have been of great uniformity. Living creatures would have remained of a like nature, and the eternal repetition of the once-created would have been the fate of most organisms. But Nature did not seem to have wanted this, so she endowed higher life with the driving force of sexuality. It meant the chance of ever new and modified individuals and, at the same time, the possibility of a change of species and forms. Thus bisexuality has been responsible in a decisive manner for the endlessly bright and protean development of life in all its branches.

THE LAWS OF HEREDITY

Today every schoolchild knows the basic principles of heredity, and we take it for granted that the characteristic traits in the offspring of plants, animals and humans, irrespective of individual differences, always resemble those of the parents. In the case of identical twins the resemblance can be so close that it is sometimes difficult to distinguish between them. It is also widely known that certain diseases and anomalies are of necessity transmitted to the progeny. On the other hand, a certain talent for music or mathematics can reappear in consecutive generations. In short, it cannot be denied that heredity often determines in a conclusive way the internal and external fate of all living creatures. But, despite its vital importance, the mystery of heredity remained unsolved until far into the nineteenth century. Since then science has made great advances and although today we know the laws which heredity obeys many problems remain to be solved. Since the main purpose of this book is to give an account of modern biology we must recall as briefly as possible the well-known facts.

The fundamental laws of heredity were first discovered by the Augustinian Father, Abbot Gregor Mendel. He published his epoch-making findings in 1865, but at the outset no one paid the slightest heed to them. It was not until 1900 that the Mendelian laws were rediscovered by the German, Correns, the Austrian, Tschermak, and the Dutchman, de Vries. The time was now ripe for the great synthesis between the study of heredity and cytology, for in the meantime chromosomes had been discovered and it was found that they behaved in exactly the same way as Mendel claimed for his inherited characters. In the monastery gardens of Brno, Mendel had experimented with various plants in an attempt to prove, among other things, how species whose sole distinguishing trait was the colour of the flower behaved when crossed. He also went into the question of how the progeny would look if two hybrids were crossed with each other or with the parent plant. These experiments led to very important results. Crossing a pure white and a pure red flowering plant gave pink offspring, the colour therefore fluctuating between white and red. This was called "intermediary" or "interparental" hereditary transmission because the characters of the hybrid stood between the parents. There were, however, other forms of transmission which came to light in Mendel's experiments. He worked initially with mathematical methods, demonstrating, for example, that in garden peas yellow seed dominates over green and round over wrinkled. The inherited characters that were not visible by no means disappeared but were to some extent concealed by others. Modern geneticists speak of "dominant" and "recessive" characters. These play a very important role in all living creatures, including man. Thus in the offspring of mixed marriages the yellow Mongolian skin has a dominance over the European white and Negro black. Dark hair has a dominance over fair hair, curly over straight hair, and brown and grey eyes over blue, etc. The "recessive" character reappears only when the respective tendencies of both parents are transmitted to the next or subsequent generations.

This is incredibly important both in theory and practice. Let us suppose, for example, that a fertilised human germ cell incorporates the father's disposition to night-blindness and the mother's normal night vision. In this case the child will also be night-blind because night-blindness is a "dominant" character and will inevitably be transmitted. Conversely, a "recessive"—in other words, hidden—inherited character, either good or bad, will "Mendelize" or come to light in a later generation. Unfavourable inheritances of this sort can be transmitted without apparent effect from one generation to the next, and then a deformity or a particular inherited disease can suddenly appear. Provided the bearers of the "recessive" factor marry only partners with a healthy background, their various children will, to outward appearances, be healthy (phenotypic). But a proportion of the offspring will have a tendency to the disease in their inheritance and will be genotypically tainted. If these marry partners with the same concealed gene, the Mendelian laws will apply in one quarter of all the possible combinations of both unfavourable genes in the germ cells. A disease potential of 25% will hold good for every child of such marriages.

No doubt there are present in the inheritance of many families bad tendencies which follow the recessive path as well as good ones. If a member of a "tainted" family marries a completely strange partner (as regards inheritance), the probability is very slight that he will possess the same hidden inherited tendencies. In the case of a marriage between first cousins, should they produce a child there is naturally a very high risk that the "black" genes will meet. A couple with the same grandparents—i.e. first cousins—will have a high percentage of the same inherited characters. Such marriages should be avoided if possible on account of this risk. In no circumstance whatever should a couple with four common grandparents marry. This comes about when two brothers marry two sisters

—a far from rare occurrence—and their children intermarry. It is clear that such a union is tantamount to "inbreeding", a highly undesirable state of affairs. Practical proof of such inbreeding has been afforded in many lands where the population lives in remote mountain districts, on small islands, or in regions where little opportunity arises for marriage with partners of different stock. Here marriages between close relatives are normal, with the shattering result that physical and mental abnormality is extraordinarily high. In families that have been investigated it is not unusual to find a third of all the children suffering from some inherited weakness.

To conclude, marriages between first cousins are always inadvisable. And, should there be diseases such as congenital epilepsy, madness, feeble-mindedness, or other inherited weaknesses in the families involved, marriages between second cousins cannot be defended either.

THE MENDELIAN LAWS

Gregor Mendel compiled the famous laws of heredity we are taught in school today. The so-called Law of Uniformity states that if we cross two strains of one species which differ in only one character (such as the colour of the flower in plants), then all the progeny in the first generation (hybrids) will display the same colours—pink, for example, when the parent plants are red and white. The progeny appear uniform, and this accounts for the term "the law of uniformity".

If the hybrids are now crossed in turn, their progeny will differ and the characters will divide. The plants will now flower red, pink and white, and the hybrids, by intermediary hereditary transmission, will segregate in the proportion of $1:2:1$, with the dominance in the proportion of 3 to 1. These figures are naturally theoretical and will not always hold good in short-term experiments. Exhaustive experiments have been carried out, entailing more than 200,000 tests. The practical results conformed quite well to the theory. This Mendelian law is known as the Law of Segregation. In our example quoted above the divergence in the colour of the flower is termed "Mendelism".

Let us now examine a further law, also discovered by Mendel —the so-called Law of Independence. Mendel crossed a tall

strain of peas which had round yellow seed with a short strain
which had green wrinkled seeds. The two races therefore
differed from each other in three respects. Starting from the
premise that the tendencies (genes) of these three pairs with
different characters had been inherited independently, such
plants would display calculable combination possibilities in the
next generation. The result of the experiment fully confirmed
the theoretical forecast: the tendencies could combine freely
with each other, and so each of the respective character distri-
butions was possible in the germ cells.

The Law of Independence provided the last proof of the
accuracy of the hypothesis that the chromosomes are in fact
the bearers of inherited characters. Paradoxically there were
cases when this did not hold good. The more scientists experimented with the phenomena of the transmission of the most
diverse characters in plants and animals, the more exceptions
were found to the Mendelian law of the free ability of inherited
characters to combine. Case after case occurred in which various characters did not divide on hybridisation but were inherited jointly. They succeeded in discovering whole groups
of characters—tied up more or less in an "inherited parcel"—
which could be jointly transmitted from generation to generation. Further research into these exceptions proved that the
number of "inherited parcels" equalled the number of the
simple chromosome set. In consequence many characters were
only inherited jointly because they resided in the same chromosomes.

This was irrefutable proof of the role of the chromosomes as
bearers of hereditary characters, and at the same time it proved
that most, or at least a great many, hereditary characters are
contained in the same chromosome. To be more precise, they
are not characters as such but hereditary units responsible for
the building up of the various characters of the organism. For
several decades now the term "gene" has been employed, and
the new discipline known as "genetics". Two peculiarities of
the gene are of great importance. The first is its capacity to
guide the development in the organism in various directions
and thereby to deploy certain prescribed characters. From
these one can trace in reverse the presence of the respective
gene. The second peculiarity is its capacity to multiply. In

this way it can produce its "like" and therefore possesses the same characteristic which we recognise as the basic phenomenon of the living substance.

THE POWER OF HEREDITARY FACTORS

The discovery of the gene not only corroborated the Mendelian laws in a brilliant manner but helped biologists to further successes, comparable only with those achieved in modern chemistry or nuclear physics. In order to understand them we must study in brief the mechanics of the transmission of inherited characters. When an ovum is fertilised by the spermatozoon the nuclei of the two cells unite. Since each nucleus contributes its own chromosome set—the genes are strung like pearls on the chromosomes—all the body cells of the future embryo must contain two chromosome sets, one from the father and one from the mother. The inheritance will, in the course of repeated division, be transmitted to all the billions of cells of which a larger organism is composed. In each fibre of our bodies is present, as it were, a reproduction of the chromosomes and genes delivered by the father and mother on fertilisation. No clearer evidence could be given of the power of heredity and of its diminutive bearers.

By so-called maturation-division, or meiosis, the new living creature grows from the fertilised ovum. But what is the position regarding the chromosome set of each cell? Since the two nuclei from which it was built each held the same number of chromosomes as the body cells of the parents, the normal figure for the living creature in question should be doubled at the union of the ovum and spermatozoon. In the next generation the chromosome set would quadruple and thus continue to increase. But in many respects this would be futile, and so Nature uses a trick to prevent such a swelling of the chromosome numbers. Meiosis takes place in the germ cells of animals, in the stamens and ovules of flowering plants, and in the spore capsules of fungi, etc. By this means chromosome inflation is avoided.

When we examine under the microscope the processes that take place in the sanctuary of life we can, subject to our experiments, observe a very strange event—the marriage of the chromosomes or, in scientific terms, the chromosome pairing.

Each chromosome from the paternal chromosome set joins with its opposite maternal number. The nucleus of the immature germ cells contains the same chromosome set as all the body cells, but when the germ cells mature they remember their origin, so to speak. For example, should the organism in question have 20 chromosomes in the body cells, then 10 pairs will be formed. At the first meiosis (reduction division) they will draw apart, leaving 2 cells, each with 10 chromosomes; these 2 cells then undergo the second meiosis (equalisation division), in which the chromosomes split lengthwise. From a still immature female germ cell, as a result of the two divisions, a total of 4 complete germ cells is formed. An ovum-forming cell delivers a single mature egg which, like the germ cells in our illustration, contains 10 chromosomes, while the "superfluous" chromosomes die. This methodology on the part of Nature is as reliable as it is thrifty. Incidentally, we have just described one of Nature's marvels which it is almost impossible to grasp.

No less marvellous and equally difficult to appreciate are the methods by which Nature impresses the various characters through the genes. The hereditary factors are apparently distributed at random among the chromosomes; genes of decisive importance, such as those that determine the length of life, lie next to others which serve for quite minor characters. The number of genes per chromosome is also very varied, some chromosomes being densely occupied while others are almost vacant. Comparatively seldom does a single gene regulate a specific character, and the latter will usually be influenced by several. Thus in the case of the geneticist's "domestic pet", the pomace fly (*drosophila melanogaster*), it has been found that a single gene can "regulate" no fewer than 5 characters, including such different objects as wing arteries and edges, the size of eyes, hair on the abdomen, or the formation of certain bristles on the creature's back. Conversely, several genes may participate in the formation of a single character. For example, the form and colour of the eyes of the drosophila are influenced by 50 different genes! When we consider that on a single giant chromosome of the fruit fly more than 1,000 genes can be detected, it is easy to see how infinitely complicated and varied the effectiveness of hereditary tendencies can be. Let us give a further example. The microscopically small germ cell of a mammal contains tens of thousands of genes. They evolved in the course of many millions of years during the development of the respective species and had to be so created that the character of every particular mammal could once more be correctly impressed in each succeeding generation. This was indeed a Herculean task, but it was carried out with uncanny accuracy and with inconceivably little consumption of material. Recent research has shown that the effective genes in modern man could be assembled in a space no larger than a pin's head.

ORGANIC CHEMISTRY CAN SOLVE THE MYSTERY OF HEREDITY

Many of these almost incredible achievements have recently been rendered basically comprehensible. The chemical foundations of hereditary processes have been studied with completely new methods, hence the term "molecular biology". This modern discipline can give us very illuminating answers to the question of how life works in its innermost laboratory. It is now known that there are two substances of a highly complex nature which play an important role in all parts of the cells which are capable of reproducing themselves and whose inherited characters can, to a certain extent, be impressed. They bear the chemical names ribonucleic acid and desoxyribonucleic acid. Since it would be tedious to write out these long words in full they have been abbreviated to RNA and DNA respectively. We shall use these abbreviations in future. DNA is contained exclusively in the chromosomes of the cell nucleus, whereas RNA is present both in the nucleus and the cytoplasm. Both these nucleic acids consist of long molecular chains in which three different groups of component parts are formed—a sugar called ribose, nitrogenous substances, and phosphoric acid.

Amalgamations of DNA with the living substance, protein, form the most important part of all cell nuclei of humans, animals and plants. DNA is obviously the decisive "bearer" of hereditary factors, its share in the substance of the cell nucleus representing the mass of genetic material. Detailed research into DNA with the aid of X-rays has invariably shown two long intertwined molecular chains. It is now accepted that in the autogeny of the genes the individual links of each chain extract

the correct building-blocks from the cell material, and so produce an exact replica of the genes. On cell division, it is passed
on to the new cell. In the light of the latest experiments this
"identical duplication" or amitosis takes place in the following
manner: the double strands of the two molecular chains of DNA
withdraw and each portion, by the acquisition of building
material, increases in size to the original double chain. Thus
one gene becomes two—and the genes regulate the specific
formation of the cells, which, for their part, unite into groups
and ultimately build up the entire organism.

Besides the actual regulating substance, DNA, the other
nucleic acid, RNA, intervenes very effectively. As far as we
can assess to date, this is achieved in the following manner.
Initially DNA takes care of the duplication of the gene; RNA
then controls the formation of the proteins needed for regulating
the further building processes—of a ferment, for example; the
nature and quantity of this ferment, as well as the moment of
its creation, then determine the formation of the further parts
of the future organism. Here it is a question above all of those
albuminoids of which the living substance, the protoplasm,
mainly consists—i.e. the proteins we have mentioned. The
word protein comes from the Greek and means "to play the
first part". An expert geneticist, G. Schramm, has recently
pointed out that this particular term is already outdated, for
the leading role in this life event is not played by the proteins
but by the two nucleic acids discussed above. They determine
the structure of the living substance, and this is a new and very
important discovery.

VIRUSES RECEIVE TELEGRAMS

We have already referred in an earlier chapter to the viruses,
those tiny creatures which feed and reproduce in the organisms
they invade and, to a certain extent, represent a kind of transitional stage between living and lifeless material. Our newly-
won knowledge of DNA and RNA has led to important practical and theoretical results in bacteriology. Apparently the
viruses regulate the building of the proteins in the invaded cell,
just as the genes did in the cell nucleus, but the cell ceases to
produce its own protein in favour of the protein of the parasite.
Viruses therefore act in the same way as genes; basically they

are genetic substance in pure cultivation, i.e. nucleic acids and protein. In the behaviour of viruses we have, so to speak, a model example of the relationship between nucleic acids and proteins, and we can investigate in particularly favourable conditions these questions, which are vital in the true sense of the word. Once more let us look at the tobacco mosaic virus. It consists of a cytoplasm containing the effective substance, the spiral nucleic acid strand. This strand is in fact a single macromolecule composed of at least 200,000 atoms.

What actually happens when such a virus attacks the plant cell? It receives the order from the alien nucleic acid to form viruses instead of the normal substance proper to the cell; and the cell does this because it carries out the orders ("information" is the scientific term) it receives under compulsion. Thus the metabolism of the invaded cell is completely changed and it produces only viruses! The next question that concerns modern geneticists is: in which of the two parts of the virus— nucleic acid or cytoplasm—is the power to infect contained? This was determined only after great difficulties, for here the entire metabolic processes of the host cell are involved. But the question was finally answered satisfactorily, with the aid of very precise modern biochemical methods, when the nucleic acids were removed from the cytoplasm without damage. They could now be subjected to experiment in isolation. It was found that they alone sufficed to induce the formation of viruses in the host cell. These viruses—and this is of extreme interest—were fully developed, and they also possessed a cytoplasm. It proves the following: that the actual "power of command" in reproductive processes of this nature is in the hands of the virus-nucleic acid. It sends telegrams to the cell substance by biochemical paths, causing the latter to produce new viruses to its own detriment. In an infection of this type a single virus particle, by constant repetition of the orders via each newly formed nucleic acid molecule, can within a week lead to the production of 100,000 billion virus particles!

HEREDITARY TENDENCIES CAN SUDDENLY CHANGE

In 1886 the Dutch botanist de Vries noted that a large number of specimens of a certain evening primrose not far from Hilversum departed from the norm. They were either

too tall or too short and displayed other very unusual devia-
tions. De Vries collected the seed from a number of these
abnormal specimens and proceeded to cultivate them. A surprising fact emerged—the offspring showed the same abnor-
malities in many subsequent generations. The characters that
had suddenly come to light were inheritable. Hereditary
changes such as these are known as mutations. They are of
major importance both in practice and theory. Countless
domestic animals and cultivated plants have originated in this
way. At one period specimens were found among normal
animals and plants which showed peculiarities in certain characters. When they were of use to man, de Vries cultivated these
examples further. In some cases the first appearance and effect
of a mutation can be actually dated. We know that in 1900,
near Zürich, a copper beech mutated from a normal beech:
this tree was the ancestor of all the copper beeches to be found
today in Switzerland and Southern Germany. Most of our hot-
house plants originated through mutation, and this applies
to every breed of dog from the Dachshund to the St. Bernard.

Such sudden hereditary changes can be important or mean-
ingless, but they invariably take place in the chromosomes.
During the first stage of meiosis accidents sometimes cause the
chromosomes to break and subsequently to repair themselves.
This can ensue in various ways: the pieces can reset upside-
down, they can attach themselves to other chromosomes, or
they can disappear completely.

Now in addition to the above form of mutation, which
merely leads to changes in the individual chromosome, there is
another which affects them all—in other words, affects the entire gene outfit. Then the whole genome will be multiplied. It
can happen that meiosis does not take place, and then the
chromosome number is not halved. When fertilisation occurs
an organism evolves with a double number of chromosomes—
this is known in genetics as a "tetraploid". In some cases this
can be repeated, and forms with chromosome outfits several times
doubled will result. These are known as polyploids. Hereditary
changes due to polyploidy are comparatively common.

Such forms very often differ in size and characters, but it is
not necessarily so. There are a host of polyploid plants which
are indistinguishable outwardly from those with a normal

chromosome number. Their vitality, however, is many times greater, and they enjoy an advantage in the struggle for survival. We know today that regions with very severe climatic conditions—the Arctic Circle, deserts, etc.—produce a large number of polyploidal forms. Such basic mutations can also be induced artificially. If we take an extract of colchicin from an autumn crocus and dip the seeds of the most diverse plants in it, polyploids usually result. The poison of the autumn crocus is a so-called mitotic poison: it attacks the mechanism of the cell division. Under its influence the chromosomes continue to divide by longitudinal fission but do not subsequently separate, so that cells with a double chromosome number result. When they divide again later they have "forgotten" that they are already double in number; they redivide, and polyploid tissue is formed. Man successfully exploited this phenomenon in his foodstuffs long before he knew of the association. The lake-dwelling peasants of the "pile-building" age were preoccupied with cultivating even heavier and richer ears of corn, and were thus responsible for the ensuing polyploid strains. It was the foundation of our intensive grain agriculture.

However, most spontaneous hereditary changes are gene mutations and their importance cannot be sufficiently emphasised, both in the positive and negative sense. To start with the latter, it is patent that a sudden change of a specific hereditary factor entails very great risks. Every creature living today is the end-product of a very lengthy evolution covering millions of years. All the applicable characters have been established, and it is obvious that the appearance of new characters, either good or bad, will somehow disrupt the harmony. Deformities can appear, organs can be so changed that they will no longer function correctly. There are, in fact, certain lethal genes which, when they appear in pure stock, can cause the death of the living organism in question. But Nature takes no heed of the individual creation. She works, one might say, from a broader standpoint—in other words, in the service of the preservation and furtherance of life. Close studies of animals and plants that have been bred for several generations and have been checked for the smallest mutations show the following results. The mutation rate lies between 0·1 % and 2 %. Some genes mutate comparatively often, while others seldom mutate. In the case of the antirrhinum 200 mutations have been recorded; in that of drosophila more than 500. We may mention a very interesting example reported by a rabbit breeder. In a litter of ordinary rabbits he found one with a very soft beaver-like fur. A new strain originated from this single specimen, which is now known as the king rabbit. Geneticists investigated this case in detail, and a very illuminating fact emerged—that the new breed of rabbit had derived from the mutation of one single gene. This is a typical example of the constant production of new characters in living creatures as the result of mutations.

MUTATIONS IN THE MOLECULE

In 1926 the American geneticist Muller produced mutations artificially by the use of X-rays on the germ cells of drosophila. He was able to prove that in this manner mutations can be substantially increased. It gave rise to a new law, according to which the percentage of new mutations depends directly upon the amount of radiation applied. Since then geneticists have found other aids to induce sudden mutations artificially. Ultra-violet rays are effective, as are the rays engendered by nuclear fission; certain chemical substances or abnormal temperatures can also be employed to the same end. These methods are now being exploited in every conceivable way to create organisms which differ from their original inherited pattern. The above-mentioned discoveries are most important, insofar as they show that it is a question of the genes functioning chemico-physically as uniform systems on a single molecule, or perhaps a molecule-like structure.

Mutation research, using the latest methods, can trace such events right back to the molecule. The following are two good examples. In a certain region of Africa the natives suffer from a serious blood infection known as drepanocytema, caused by a change in the chemical structure of the hæmoglobin. The disease is hereditary, and the symptoms reveal a difference in the shape of the red blood corpuscles, which instead of being round as normally, are crescent-shaped. The appearance of the disease was due to a mutation, and once more the special feature is that the change concerns only one gene. This particular gene has the important task of regulating the formation of hæmoglobin. When this hereditary factor underwent a change for the worse by mutation a disturbance in the production of the red corpuscles was the result. At a certain spot in the hæmoglobin molecule a single one of the 300 protein building-blocks (amino-acids) changed, and this apparently trifling disturbance in the otherwise normal building of hæmoglobin was enough to interfere seriously with its function. The red blood corpuscles degenerated into crescent-shaped cells. Here one can really say that little causes can have great effects.

A second up-to-date method of research into the chemistry of mutation uses viruses as experimental subjects. We have already seen that these minute creatures are specially suited for such purposes because they have the advantage of representing living molecules. Genetic and hereditary problems can be studied in extremely favourable conditions, for if such a molecule is changed by experiment the "information" given as a result of the influence of the virus on the cytoplasm of the host cell must also change. In this way mutations can, so to speak, be engendered in the test tube. In fact, it has recently been done and we now have a completely new technique, of which the practical and theoretical significance cannot be over-estimated.

Let us once more take for our purpose the virus of the tobacco mosaic disease because, it will be remembered, its actual effective substance is RNA. When treated with suitable chemical agents the structure of its molecule changes. The burning question was whether such an effect also influences the genetic characters of the virus and consequently its power to infect the attacked cell. Two chances open before us. We can carry out an intensive research into the important problems of mutation and, at the same time, explore new possibilities for fighting these extremely dangerous disease agents. This new work has brought amazing success in both fields.

It was found, to begin with, that a chemical change of the RNA of the tobacco mosaic virus actually induced mutations, and to an astonishingly high degree. Comparatively small influences of this nature led to the conclusion that the virus strains serving as "guinea pigs" could, in terms of heredity, be changed up to 80%. This was the first time that direct experiment succeeded in inducing mutations in a molecule. Further development of this important method of theoretical research will open up new possibilities of a practical nature. We can now expect that artificially mutated viruses will be used for combating the lethal varieties. Even more important is the second possibility. It is well known that there are countless dangerous diseases that effect humans and are caused by viruses. This applies, in particular, to the epidemics polio-myelitis, smallpox, yellow fever, rabies and psittacosis, not to mention infectious diseases such as measles, chicken pox or mumps. Should it now become possible, by artificial mutation of the disease-causing characters of such viruses, to "cultivate" harmless strains, then we can work out quite new methods of immunisation. As everyone knows, smallpox, which was once the terror of all civilised countries, is much less dreaded today because children have been innoculated with a harmless vaccine which protects them from infection by the true pox.

After the recent successes with the experimental generation of mutated virus strains, we can expect the molecules of the viruses in question to be changed and rendered quite harmless. These harmless breeds can then serve to protect the organism against the "genuine" variety and to render these dangerous disease agents innocuous. In the present case, the objective research into the fundamentals of organic chemistry seems to afford a chance of its being put to great practical use. The systematic study of mutations began with experiments on dro-sophila, but now this purely biological work has far surpassed its original goals and promises mankind new and effective aids in his struggle against disease.

CHAPTER IV

The Development of Life

OUR craving for sensation is more than adequately catered for today. Some of us would probably be grateful if, for a day or two, no exciting news were to be announced in the Press and on the air. . . . But in the old days, in more "peaceful" times, there were often periods during which reporters chewed their pens because there was absolutely nothing to write about. In such cases there was always one standby, and even today they will occasionally fall back on the ever successful story—of the good old sea serpent or monster turning up somewhere, or of an octopus of a size never before encountered being sighted, or of the recently returned traveller, Mr. X, who in some remote primeval forest, has caught a glimpse of an animal no human eye has previously seen. However improbable such *a priori* reports may be, in most cases they still find credence, for the infinite variety of life and its creations is so fantastic that the borderline between fiction and fact is at times difficult, even for the professional scientist, to define. Our planet houses a vast number of plants and animals and every imaginable form and stage of life is to be found on its surface. A million-and-a-half species have already been catalogued, and their number is by no means complete.

This huge figure applies only to living creatures inhabiting the earth today, and therefore only to a small sector of the billion-year history of life. Countless animal and plant phyla originated and disappeared in earlier geological ages. Although we have discovered about half a million fossilised remains of animals, we can safely conclude that their total number was many times greater. But these finds are positive proof of one fact—that the organisms in their great variety have certainly not always been the same. Admittedly many of them have preserved their present-day form since time immemorial, but the most important forms, the great dynasties of animals and plants, were once very different in character and appearance.

The British writer H. G. Wells once published a very exciting novel, *The Time Machine*. This was about an apparatus that enabled one to go back in time to any required period. If such an apparatus were at our disposal today and we could travel back in time to the Cretaceous, we should meet with fabulous creatures which bear little or no resemblance to our familiar flora and fauna. We have only to recall the strange race of Saurians, those gigantic creatures that roamed the primeval world. It would be fatal were we, in our time machine, to meet with a Tyrannosaurus, the largest carnivore to have existed on earth. It was about 45 ft. long and 15 ft. high. Its huge skull contained fearsome teeth, and all the terror-arousing features formerly attributed to the dragon were united in this creature. Nor would it be very pleasant to meet a Diplodocus, one of the dinosaurs, which weighed 39 tons, or a Brontosaurus, which had a length of some 65 ft.

Fiction writers have told exciting stories of unexplored jungles where single specimens of these terrifying monsters have survived, but in actual fact the dinosaurs have been extinct for more than 70 million years. "Dinosaur" comes from the Greek words *deinos* (terrifying), and *sauros* (lizard). They disappeared completely from the face of the earth just after the Cretaceous, unfortunately leaving us only their rather pathetic descendants, the present-day reptiles—for what is the largest extant crocodile compared with those monstrous earlier reptiles? In their innumerable strange forms they lived on land, in the water and in the air during the "Middle Ages" of the earth. In addition to the giant saurians, flying lizards, etc., there were also small dinosaurs. The fossilised remains of one, not much bigger than an ordinary domestic cat, have recently been found.

But 70 million years means very little when we let our minds wander back in time to those inconceivably remote periods when life began on our planet. At the very beginning the "living molecules" must have been born, followed by the single-celled plants and animals to which we have already referred. Of these probionta no trace, of course, remains, and we can only reconstruct their existence by deduction. In the earth's oldest geological formations certain graphite seams give some hints to the existence of algæ. The pre-Cambrian is the first to

provide us with rather indeterminate remains of living creatures, but from the earth's "antiquity" we have a wealth of
evidence in the form of fossils, etc. From them it appears that
the earliest living creatures lived exclusively in the water.
Their evolutionary history goes very far back in time, and in
the Cambrian and Silurian representatives of all phyla, with
the exception of the vertebrates, were present. At that period
strange arthropods, such as the Trilobites, and giant crabs 6 ft.
6 ins. long, corals, sponges, echinoderms, molluscs, etc.,
peopled the water. The plants, on the other hand, had not
advanced above the level of organisation of the algæ. The first
vertebrates appeared in the Silurian—strangely-shaped arm-
oured fish, which died out in the Devonian; remote ancestors of
the shark; and also a very remarkable creature which we shall
now consider more closely.

THE REMARKABLE STORY OF THE CŒLACANTH

In December, 1938, the woman curator of the Natural History Museum of East London, South Africa, was examining
a few specimens of the smaller sharks. They had been caught
by the crew of a fishing-boat and were delivered to her as
zoological material. But on this occasion she found a very remarkable fish among the sharks. It was about 6 ft. long, with a
prominent lower jaw and unusual fins that looked uncommonly like atrophied legs. The curator had never seen such a
fish before, nor could she find its description in any of the books
in the museum library. She preserved her interesting find,
made a drawing of it, and sent it with the necessary data to one
of the best-known icthyologists, Professor Smith. This scholar
was in for one of the greatest shocks of his life. "I could hardly
have been more surprised had I met a dinosaur in the street!"
was his first comment after comparing the drawing with fossilised impressions of primeval fish. The Professor took the next
plane to East London, examined the preserved specimen, and
found that his diagnosis had been correct. It was a so-called
"tassel-fin", or cœlacanth, whose relatives had existed 300
million years ago and which, in the opinion of zoologists, was
long since extinct. But now one of these creatures had been
fished up out of the sea and looked very little different from its
pre-historic ancestors.

It was naturally a scientific sensation of the first order. Every measure was taken to ensure that further examples of this fish, so remarkable in every respect, might be found. A pamphlet was printed, giving a description in three languages of the cœlacanth, together with its photograph, and offering a 400 dollar reward for the delivery of a similar specimen. At this point the Second World War broke out, and men had other cares to occupy them than the hunt for an interesting fish. At the end of the war the search for the cœlacanth was resumed. It lasted for many years without success, but on December 23rd, 1952, Professor Smith received the telegram for which for so many years he had hoped. The sender was the captain of a British merchant ship trading in the Indian Ocean. The text of the message was: "Have cœlacanth in the Comoros. Please collect immediately."

This was easier said than done, since Zanzibar, where Professor Smith lived at the time, is 3,500 miles from the Comoro Islands in the Indian Ocean. But the Prime Minister of the Union of South Africa placed an aircraft at Professor Smith's disposal, so that he was able to reach the place of the new discovery in time. The cœlacanth now became an international sensation. The reward for further specimens of the prehistoric fish was doubled, and a host of pamphlets describing it were distributed in all the likely ports. It now turned out that these creatures were well known to the natives. They had often caught them but had found only a trivial use for them— their sharp scales were ideal for scraping punctured bicycle inner-tubes before patching.

The fishermen now saw a reward which represented their normal income of about three years. No wonder, then, that the hunt for the cœlacanth became the major preoccupation of countless natives, with the result that in recent years several more specimens have been caught. In the development of its feet-like fins it shows a potential capacity for very considerable individual mutations. Corroboration of this "adaptability" in the cœlacanth is important, as we shall see. The man to whom we owe ·the identification of this living fossil, Professor Smith, made the following comments on it: "In the cœlacanth we have the nearest living relative of a long-extinct fish, which must be considered as one of the ancestors of the mammals. It is in the direct evolutionary line of the ancestors of man." It seems worth while therefore to consider in great detail the very remarkable kinship, for it concerns nothing less than the development of life.

As we know, life began in the water, and there were billions of years at the disposal of these aquatic animals for their development. And then one day something new happened. One of them went ashore. It certainly did not do so of its own free will—only under dire compulsion—because the water was its natural element, its home. Certain conditions must have developed which were so unfavourable that the fear of them was stronger than the fear of the unknown. Such conditions could arise on the seashores, in the marshes and lagoons, as well as in the alluvial deltas of the larger river estuaries.

In the Silurian there was a long period of great drought. The sea receded, and on the littoral vast marshes were formed, consisting of a great deal of mud and little water—conditions in which there was not enough oxygen to keep the gill-breathing fish alive. This was very hard indeed for the aquatic animals which happened to be stranded in such regions. Their way back to the sea was cut off and there remained only one chance of survival—flight from the primeval slime to the land. This sounds stranger than it really is, for even today, in some of the mangrove swamps of Africa, there are fish able to climb trees and remain for long periods out of the water. Whales, on the other hand, are mammals which have returned to the sea, but as they possess lungs instead of gills they have to surface at regular intervals to take in air. Their ancestors were four-footed and lived on *terra firma*.

But to return to our cœlacanth. It was, in fact, the only fish of its period which had a chance of surviving the crisis in the marshes. This remarkable creature has to thank the development of special, and to a certain extent supplementary, tendencies in its organism. As we have already said, the cœlacanth possesses feet-like fins, by whose aid its ancestors could cross the dry parts of the lagoons. In addition it possesses an auxiliary apparatus for taking in oxygen, which biologists call vascular lungs. It also has a third peculiarity—the rudiments of a cerebrum at the base of the skull.

We do not know how long this evolutionary trend took, nor

shall we ever know for certain. Time was no object. In any case, the cœlacanth eventually became the first vertebrate to accomplish the transition from water to dry land. In the ensuing 300 million years this had the most remarkable results. From the cœlacanths are descended the first four-legged batrachians from which, in two branches, developed the extant batrachians and the reptiles. From the reptile branch there was an early separation into mammals, and a later separation into birds, whose original relationship with reptiles can still be recognised by a host of common features. According to everything we know today, this development would have taken place in a completely different manner had not the initial step on to *terra firma* been taken by those clumsy but adaptable creatures, the cœlacanths. This, then, is the fish that succeeded in conquering dry land, to become, at the same time, the ancestor of the great groups of land animals. Moreover, this truly versatile fish has miraculously continued to exist in a very slightly changed form as an aquatic animal for millions of years—in fact until today. Science was prepared to offer 800 dollars for a newly caught cœlacanth, and on reflection this seems a very cheap price to pay.

THE DWARFS TAKE OVER FROM THE GIANTS

Animal life without plants is impossible. Consequently there must have been land plants before the animals could leave their original element, water. After the so-called Age of the Algæ, which extended far into the Upper Silurian, we find fossils of those growths known as silver ferns (gymnogramme). They had not yet developed into stalk and leaf, but ingenious Nature gave them a particular apparatus that enabled them at a given moment to colonise the damp littoral. These remarkable protista possessed vascular tissue for the distribution of sap and formed shoots which rose into the air above the water: to allow breathing they had special fissures.

Therefore, to a certain extent, this was a transitional stage. Later, followed plants which could develop true roots, leaves and a well-functioning "water supply" system. They had plenty of time to achieve this. On the mainland, in the Devonian, there were already true ferns, horsetails and lycopodia, many of which have proved remarkably hardy and remain almost unchanged today, after 300 million years. From other forms of this type, during the Carboniferous, developed those great sigillaria and lepidendra to which, together with the giant horsetails, we owe a considerable part of our coal deposits. Giant animals also inhabited the great marshes, and Nature, for some particular reason, showed a predilection for giants at this period. Huge salamanders crawled along the ground and powerful insects—for example, dragonflies with a wingspan of 31 inches—whirred through the air.

The record in this trend towards gigantism was reached with the saurians, whose peak was in the earth's Middle Ages. We have already mentioned some of their representatives, but there were many more on the earth, in the water, and in the air. (One of the flying lizards, the Pteranodon, had a wing-span of 26 feet.) The saurians conquered all the living space with the exception of the cold regions unsuited to them, increasing to even greater size in the Cretaceous, and then suddenly dying out.

Their successors were creatures which had existed unobtrusively for a long time in the shadow of the giants and belong to the mammal class. In physical structure they first resembled certain reptile groups—such primitive creatures had already existed since the Jurassic, but in comparison with the all-conquering saurians they were quite insignificant. At about the beginning of the Tertiary (i.e. some 60 million years ago) Nature embarked upon something new—her great and, so far, last experiment in the creation of new forms of life. This was the experiment with mammals, and finally with man.

Early in the Tertiary the proto-mammals appeared—animals of fairly simple construction, the size of a sheep, with short legs, a long tail, and the teeth of omnivores. From them three equally primitive groups evolved—the proto-birds, the proto-carnivores and the proto-insectivores. Down the ages a great wealth of new types and forms appeared. They were each adapted to certain prescribed living conditions and types of food, until finally these mammals took over the living space of the earth. This applied also to the cold regions, whose severe conditions warm-blooded animals could tolerate.

A typical example of the astounding evolutionary changes in a living creature towards ever greater perfection, of the change from simple to complicated types of organisation, can be seen in the development of the horse. At the beginning of the Tertiary it was a forest-dweller the size of a fox, with short legs and ten toes. Thanks to a series of fossils, we can determine how the modern horse developed down the ages from its primeval form. It increased in size, its legs grew longer, and at the same time the five toes of the original "paw" developed to a single unit, the hoof. This is an admirable contrivance for fast movement. The fossil shows precisely how the middle toe developed more and more to that mighty "fingernail"—the hoof as it appears today—after the degeneration of the remaining toes. All this can be proved in detail, thanks to North American finds ranging from the upper Tertiary to the Diluvian.

THE UPWARD PATH

The development of mammals and birds, which began in the Cretaceous, progressed by leaps and bounds from the Tertiary onwards to ever more complex forms. The mighty dinosaurs never returned, although the cave bear, giant stag, proto-elephant and mammoth, attained very considerable proportions in comparison with modern forms of animal life. But what the new "ruling group" of mammals lacked in externals they replaced to an increasing extent by the development of a far more important characteristic: they became more intelligent, and their brains increased in size and ramification. Thus they were better suited to survive in the struggle for existence than the clumsy saurians. Measurements have shown that these primitive giants had very small brains, most of them no larger than a child's hand. The post-Tertiary mammals were far superior to the saurians in this respect. Plants also began to show an increasing refinement. Lepidendra, horsetails and sigillaria were replaced by more highly organised types, the deciduous trees began to develop, and finally, in the course of æons, the wealth of present-day flowering plants evolved.

Whether or not the formation of the basic types of life followed at random on an individual plane, one thing is clear, that in the course of evolution they made great strides towards perfection. The path led upwards, from comparatively unknown origins to the partially known, and finally from mysterious intermediate stages to the present-day forms of life. At times this path led into error, with the resultant exaggerations such as the inordinately huge saurians and the over-weighty horns of the primitive animals. They were episodic developments, and most of the errors were rectified in the course of time by the creation of efficiently armed living creatures of greater variety and refinement. The "centralising control" in the higher animals increased until finally it gave rise to the central nervous system in birds and mammals. At the top of this evolutionary ladder stands man, who broke out of the biological circle and, with his culture, reached the pinnacle in the development of life.

This is how the upward path is seen today. Is it merely theory, or can we bring proofs to bear to substantiate such statements? The onus, above all, is on the palæontologists, who, in the light of their fossil finds from the various geological periods, can afford us a glimpse of the enormous graduation of life. This is no easy task, for the extinct ancestors of our present-day animals and plants were not kind enough to leave fossilised traces, bones, etc., in accessible places. As today, most of the living creatures were completely destroyed after their deaths, and it was a matter of pure chance when the circumstances and the environment in which these primitive animals and plants died allowed their remains to be at least partially preserved for millions of years.

For example, it was a pure stroke of luck that the fossil of the famous archæopteryx found in the schist of Solenhofen turned out to be a true intermediate form, a transition in the development from one stage to another. Exponents of the theory of evolution deduced from certain similarities in construction of this animal group that from the former saurians developed crocodiles, lizards, snakes, etc., along one line and birds along the other—animals, in fact, so basically different that one seemed perfectly entitled to question such a theory. But the Solenhofen find afforded conclusive proof, for this fossil bird is at once lizard and flier. It has feathers but, as opposed to all living birds, vertebræ in the tail, well-developed claws on the wings and a particularly lizard-like row of teeth in its jaws. Another extremely lucky find was made in the Gobi Desert. A kind of giant graveyard of dinosaurs was discovered. Presumably some natural catastrophe had overtaken them, with the result that we now have many magnificently preserved remains.

Incidentally, there can be no question of a complete and fool-proof ancestral tree being compiled with the aid of fossils dis-covered to date. This is the dream of the scientist, but it will never be fulfilled. Actually we very rarely find in the "chronicle of the rocks" intermediate stages such as the above fossil birds. Almost invariably the fossils are examples of a specific, fully developed species and its relatives. Palæontologists may dis-cover a great number of these, but the intermediate forms, the transitions—above all, between the great groups of living creatures—are almost entirely lacking. This circumstance in itself makes a strong case for the theory of rapid change, and against a slow development following step by step via many intermediate stages. The history of fossils continually shows that on the introduction of new building plans an "explosive phase" occurs in which, in a comparatively short space of geological time, completely new types of living creatures ap-pear. The differentiation and specialisation of the new basic types then proceed over very lengthy periods. Apparently the building plans of living creatures followed in fairly quick suc-cession in the springtime of the earth's history, for during its antiquity the prototypes of the great races of animals and plants were already present. The decisive question now is: wherein lie the causes of this development?

DARWIN AND THE THEORY OF EVOLUTION

Even the great naturalist Linnaeus, to whom we owe the foundation of our biological systematics, was convinced that the present-day animals and plants had existed on the earth from the beginning "because children invariably bear some re-semblance to their parents". Not until the 18th century did Cuvier recognise that the remains of primitive animals which occasionally came to light were no "whims of Nature," as had been formerly thought. He came to the revolutionary con-clusion for his age that in earlier periods quite other organisms peopled the earth. According to him, a whole series of natural catastrophes, and the ensuing creative periods, produced on each occasion new dwellers on our planet who had nothing to do with those who had gone before.

Lamarck pointed out his error, but Charles Darwin in his famous work *The Origin of Species by Means of Natural Selection* (1859) was the first to make the so-called evolutionary theory— the accuracy of which can no longer seriously be denied today —a part of modern natural science. We should like to point out that the theory of evolution as such—i.e. the theory of transformation and development of the species—is here meant, and not the so-called "Darwinism" which attempted to explain the primary causes for the metamorphosis of the species on the basis of the Darwinian theory. This part of the Darwinian theory gave rise to a bitter controversy which is not yet re- solved today. Darwin's theories, above all the theory of natural selection in the struggle for existence, have even become ques- tions of an "outlook on life". In fact Darwin's theory cannot be summed up in the statement that man is descended from the monkey—this he never maintained; nor did he see the struggle for existence in terms of economic strife. In order to avoid these popular errors we must make it clear that Darwinism today is understood primarily as the theory of natural selection, a theory which is still being contested. What proof can the theory of evolution offer for its accuracy?

Despite the diversity of life on earth its forms show a greater or lesser resemblance, and the classification of living creatures is arranged according to such considerations. The smaller the systematic unit (species, genus, family, etc.), the greater the similarity of the animals or plants belonging to it. For example, the bone structure of the forelimbs of a man, a bear and a bat show certain peculiarities typical to the mammals. Only in individual cases are the bones formed differently, according to the purpose for which they are to be used—to grasp, walk, or fly. Obviously, then, at some period in time there was a single basic type, a "blueprint" for these limbs which, in the course of development and according to the purpose required, became subject to differentiation. Time after time we find the same bones, whether they be in specialised or atrophied form. The number of "toes" alternates between one and five.

THE MUSEUM IN OUR BODIES

The human body provides a wealth of proofs for the evolu- tionary theory. It is in fact a museum, in which a whole series of "memories" of earlier stages in the development of man from different forms of life are preserved. Thus we carry about with us organs which, from the present-day standpoint, are quite pointless and must be considered purely as relics. A rudimentary feature, for example, is our coccyx. This consists of a number of small atrophied bones located at the base of the spine and connected to the pelvis. They serve no purpose to-day and yet they are the remains of a very important organ, the tail. The blood vessels and sinews which originally served it are still there in the neighbourhood of the coccyx, and for a short time the human embryo actually possesses a tail-like formation.

Further examples are the muscles and the shape of our ears. The outer rim of the ear in most men rises to a small point, known as Darwin's tubercle of the auricle. This is the last vestige of the long pointed ears which we find in the horse, in cattle or in dogs. Some people of course can waggle their ears, and this is a reminder of the ability to point the ears in the direction of a sound, as we can observe in an excited horse. In man, however, this neglected muscle for moving the ears is pointless, just as are the other museum pieces such as the vermiform appendix, some of the stomach muscles, the course of certain blood vessels and much else in our bodies.

Similar proofs in favour of the evolutionary theory offered by vestigial organs are to be found in many other animals. The whale, for instance, has no legs, but this marine mammal developed from a four-footed land-dweller and retains, as a "memory", the vestigia of a pelvic girdle. To this the legs were attached when they were used by its forbears on dry land. The blind mole still has eyes under its fur, the flightless ostrich still has wing-like bones, etc. All these purposeless structures in the bodies of animals of today would be incomprehensible unless taken in the context of the evolutionary theory as vestigia of organs that were once used by differently constructed ancestors.

Of particular interest are the vestigial "memories" which occur during embryonic development. They are merely detours which serve no intrinsic purpose and represent an abridged repetition of earlier stages of life. Thus the embryos of the adder have stunted hind legs which disappear during further development, and the blood circulation system in the embryos of mammals and birds initially shows a typical tendency towards the branchial arteries of the fish, even to the formation of the so-called branchial clefts. Man, of course, has no further use for gills: nevertheless in the embryo the bases are there as though a fish would develop. They finally degenerate completely and no trace of gills appears in the newborn child.

The development therefore initially recalls the fish stage and a subsequent change of mind for something better. In certain individuals the degeneration of the branchial clefts is incomplete, and they retain two small openings in the throat throughout their lives. It is a very unpleasant condition because it can so easily lead to branchial fistulas, which cause tiresome disturbances. A harmless reminder of the earlier stages in the development of man is the "Lanugo down", a silky fleece covering the whole body of the embryo about three months before birth, leaving only the face, the palms of the hands, and the soles of the feet clear.

THE CONVICT AND THE TORTOISES

As a young naturalist Darwin made a voyage round the world and was able to work for several months on the Galapagos Islands. He was fascinated by the giant tortoises which lived there in great numbers, and he killed a few specimens from each island to take back to his museum at home. They were laid out to dry on the beach. One day a boatload of convicts arrived from a neighbouring island, where they lived in lonely exile. One of the men was immediately able to tell Darwin from which island the various tortoises came and to point out the features which distinguished them according to their place of origin. This was one of the most important facts that led Darwin to postulate his great theory. From now on he could not rid himself of the suspicion that once upon a time, when the Galapagos group was still a single mass, only one species of tortoise lived there. Not until the sea bed sank and the uniform population of tortoises was split up into several isolated groups could changes, involving many centuries, take place in the inherited characters of the tortoises on the various islands. In this principle of isolation Darwin had discovered a factor which still provides us today with one of the most important contributions to an understanding of the origin of species.

Most jellyfish originate from a small polyp attached to the sea bed. The polyp reproduces asexually (by budding) and sexually (by ova and spermatozoa), releasing male and female jellyfish. New polyps form from the fertilized ova of the latter, and so the process continues. Our picture shows a polyp tree; the budding jellyfish are clearly visible.

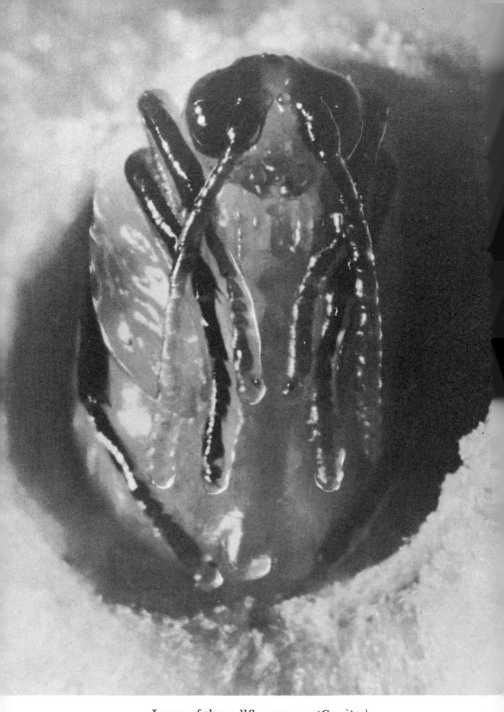

Larva of the gallfly or wasp. *(Cynips.)*

Pupa of the lunar-headed dung beetle. *(Copris lunaris.)*

These pictures show h
the embryo chicken dev
ops in the egg shell.

Upper: After 7½ broc
ing days the embryo he.
can be clearly seen in t'
bloodshot yolk. In the ce
ter of the eye the ma
components are alreac
developed.

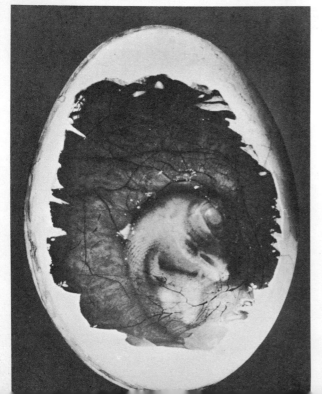

Lower: After 12 broodin;
days the shape of th
future chicken is recogniz
able. Below the eye can b
seen the outer orifice o
the ear. The organs of th
blood circulation and di
gestive system are already
formed at this stage.

Facing page: The chick 1
day before hatching. The
tiny creature now com-
pletely fills the egg and
there is no space left. As a
bird that leaves the nest
immediately after hatch-
ing, it is already equipped
to find its own food shortly after emergence from
the egg. Its legs are more
powerful than those of
other fledglings which remain in the nest to be fed.

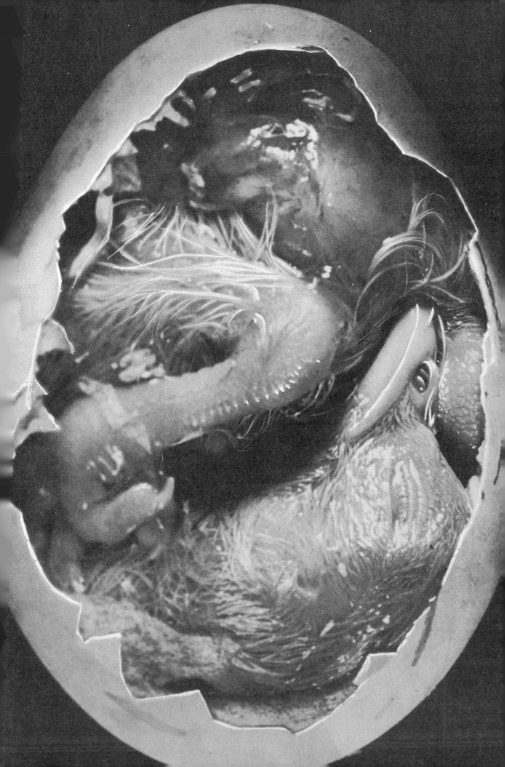

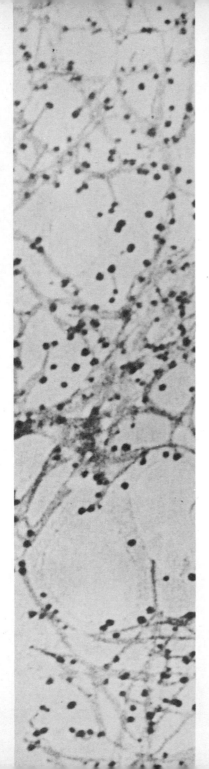

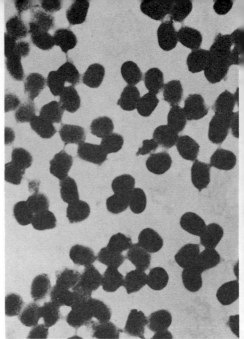

DIMINUTIVE ENEMIES

Among the most dangerous foes of mankind, domestic animals and cultivated plants, are the tiny disease agents known as viruses. They cannot be seen except under an electron microscope. With the aid of the latter, viruses can now be photographed. Our plates show:

Left: Tobacco-mosaic virus (enlarged 30,000 times).

Above: Smallpox virus.

Facing page: The cause of the dreaded poliomyelitis, or infantile paralysis.

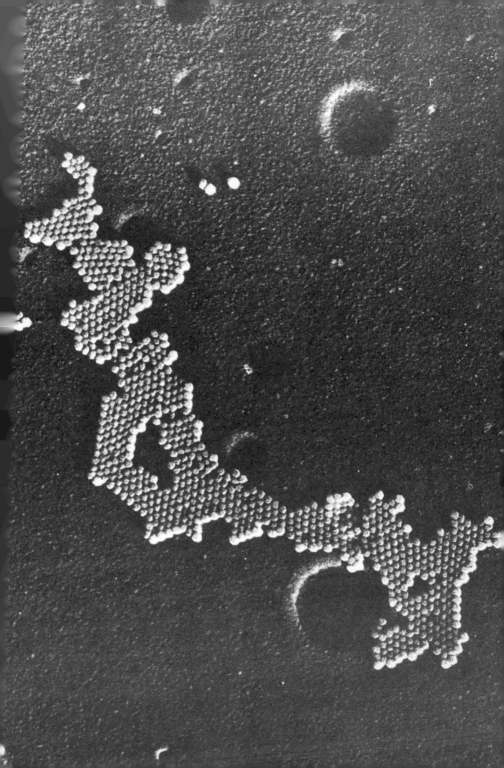

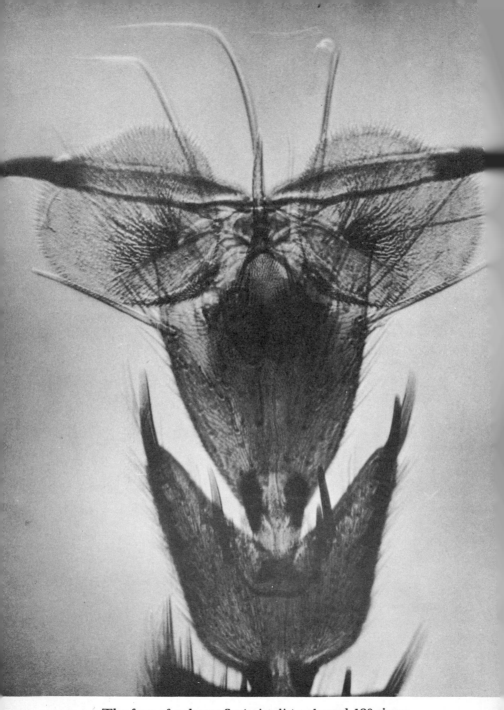

The foot of a drone fly *(eristalis)* enlarged 120 times.

In 1938 the cœlacanth, a fish which has become famous, was caught for the first time off the coast of Africa. The species was believed to have been extinct for several million years. This was an error. The photographs show full-length and front views of this prehistoric fish.

Amber, the resin dripping from wounds in the trees of Tertiary forests (about 40 million years ago), has preserved many objects which today provide us with information about prehistoric life. This and the following two pages show comparisons between insects imprisoned in amber and their living counterparts. The likenesses are very striking.

Above: A capricorn beetle (cerambycidae) in amber.
Below: The same insect today.

A spider in amber.

A robber spider today.

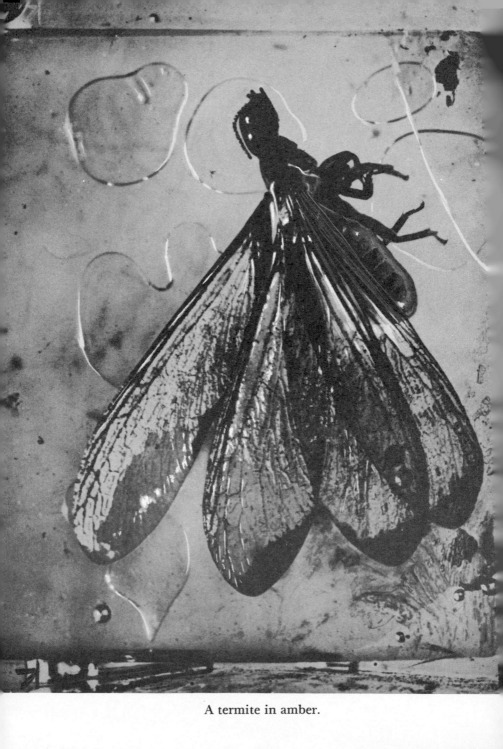

A termite in amber.

Let us imagine a large living space, at first colonised equally by the representatives of an animal or plant species. We then discover among countless individuals the signs of the particular species intermingled in great variety. Since the members of the same species can multiply—this is their most important characteristic, although the rule can occasionally be broken— all the hereditary stigmata will be constantly intermingled. The species as a whole, however, retains its uniform stamp. If then for some reason the original living space is split into various separated areas, as in the case of the Galapagos Islands, the living conditions in the individual areas will differ somewhat with regard to temperature, moisture and food supplies.

Down the ages, then, the original uniform species, as a result of spatial isolation of the different groups of its members and of differentiated selection, will split into countless strains which may finally differ so greatly from the original species that breeding between the newly evolved strains will no longer be possible. In this way, by ever widening racial differences, new species more and more separated from each other will evolve. On isolated islands and archipelagos we very often find such species. The Hawaiian Islands offer a famous example. There we find 445 types of snails, of which all but one are types endemic to that group. Of the 729 species of plant, 575 are peculiar to Hawaii.

Australia, a continent cut off from all other land masses, has developed an animal world of its own. On this giant "island" we find a great variety of strange marsupials (kangaroo, pouched wolf, wombat, etc.). It was a development which ran parallel to the remaining mammals but which created numerous specialised forms. We often meet, too, in areas which for long periods have been cut off from the main stream of evolution by some natural barrier such as the sea or high mountains, special features in the organisms living there. Millions of years ago, when the Alps formed, the plants of the Asiatic high mountain ranges began to colonise Europe, with the result that our Alpine flora today has much in common with them. In the course of the ages our Alpine plants, separated from their original Asiatic home, have formed many new species. More than 30% of them are peculiar to the European Alps. A host of such proofs of an evolutionary development are available.

THE FIRST CAUSES OF EVOLUTIONARY DEVELOPMENT

Darwin's achievements were extraordinary, to say the least, because he was able to offer his hypothesis of the evolution of life within the bare framework of the science of his day, and in those days the biologist was ignorant of much of what is taken for granted today as the basis for such reflections. A little over a hundred years ago, when his *magnum opus* appeared, comparatively few fossils relating to the origins of life were available, and practically nothing was known of the actual nature of the hereditary processes. Cattle breeders, of course, had a certain experience to guide them, but no biologist could tell them what laws came into play. Nevertheless Darwin recognised the step-by-step origin of the species, and his basic concept has been completely justified by modern research. But how do matters stand regarding the original causes of evolutionary development? How did it happen and what were the main factors?

First and foremost there was the well known "environment theory" of Lamarck. This was based on the undisputed fact that living creatures are often amazingly well-adapted to their environment—in other words, to their prevailing surroundings, food sources, climate, etc. It was suggested that the living conditions themselves must have led directly to this adaptability. Lamarck quoted a famous example, the case of the giraffe with its abnormally long neck. His explanation ran roughly as follows. The ancestors of the modern giraffe originally had quite normal necks. At some early period a very dry climate ruled in their African habitat, the grass of the steppe dried up, and only the foliage of the trees remained to them as food. In order to reach as much of this as possible the proto-giraffes craned their necks to the utmost, and only those which best performed this acrobatic feat survived. The extension of the giraffe's neck by long practice was now transmitted at least to a certain proportion of the descendants, which, for their part, were forced to continue the neck-stretching process during the protracted drought. In due course, therefore, the animals acquired their extraordinarily useful necks.

This is an example of the much quoted "inheritance of acquired characters", the most important pillar of the Lamarckian theory. It is based on the fact that the experience of individuals leads to a definite adaptability of their organs, etc., to prescribed environmental conditions. Boxers and wrestlers develop remarkably exaggerated torsos, the fur of animals grows thicker in long periods of cold . . . In the course of time the environment made new claims to which living creatures had to adapt themselves.

According to Lamarck it followed that the function of an organ directly affects its formation. The example of the giraffe's neck confirms this premise, as in his opinion do the legs of the flamingo, which grew to stilt-like proportions because the bird stood perpetually in water and had to stretch its legs to keep its body dry. Conversely, the failure to use organs leads to their degeneration and, finally, to their loss. That is why, according to the theory, the inhabitants of dark caves eventually went blind, since they no longer had any use for eyes. Today this theory has few adherents, for the findings of the geneticists in animal and plant breeding contradict it. It is possible that in certain cases Lamarck's accepted "functional adaptability" plays a part, but as an important or unique original cause of the origin of new species it cannot hold good in the light of our present knowledge.

THE STRUGGLE FOR EXISTENCE

Darwin himself saw the solution of the problem in natural selection through the struggle for existence. We are all familiar with one form of selection in the breeding of our domestic pets. The dachshund or the fox terrier, the bantam or the pouter pigeon, have evolved from a conscious selection and further breeding of animals possessing certain characters. This encouraged Darwin to extend the idea of the selection made in breeding domestic animals to the great problem of the creation of new forms in wild Nature. He held that, in the vast periods of time during which life developed on earth, Nature herself undertook a "natural breeding selection" and, through the struggle for existence, selected the most suitable living creatures.

Her task was made easier by the tremendous capacity to procreate of nearly all organisms, in particular of insects, as we have already mentioned. So much issue is put into the world by animals and plants everywhere that only a small proportion of them can survive; otherwise, within a comparatively short time, a single group of living creatures would fill the earth at the expense of all the others. In this connection Darwin showed that even the slow-breeding elephant is no exception to the rule. During her long life the elephant cow gives birth on an average to six calves. Were she and her entire issue to remain alive, then (Darwin made precise calculations) in the short span of 750 years (short in geological time) a single pair of elephants would have about 19 million progeny. Nature therefore continually scatters an extravagant wealth of life upon the earth and, at the same time, allows this life to be destroyed in a thousand ways—in the struggle for food, by enemies, diseases, the effects of climate, etc. Countless measures of this type see to it—provided man does not interfere—that an ecological balance is maintained, that one species cannot increase disproportionately at the expense of others.

In the constant grim struggle for existence throughout the whole of Nature, only a small percentage of the excessive issue of animals and plants survives in each individual case. It is obvious that these "victors" are not the weakest specimens. As a general rule, when no external accidents take a decisive hand the best issue survives for procreation. Darwin accepts a sexual selection only in so far as the usual "excessive supply" of males allows the females a certain choice. The strongest, handsomest or, in some respects, most capable male will have better prospects for procreation than competitors with less attraction for the females. In this way the selection and furtherance of the desired characters are increased.

According to Darwin the origin of countless weapons in the male animal (horns, tusks, etc.) plays an important part in sexual selection. The strongest animal possessing the best weapon will not only have a particular attraction for the female, but in its bitterly fought contest with other males prior to mating—think for a moment of rutting stags—it will have the best chance of victory and of bequeathing its characters to the progeny. Conversely, in wild Nature, weak or sick animals and plants are very quickly eliminated. Most of our highly bred domestic animals are "weak" in this sense. It is not rare for runaway pets to turn wild. After a few generations the characters imposed by man are shed and the pets revert to their original type.

A particularly refined form of the struggle for existence is displayed in the protective and warning colours of animals, above all in mimicry. These phenomena were claimed by Darwin and his school as one of the most striking confirmations for the theory of natural selection. Since it deals with an enchanting side of biology, let us take a closer look at these remarkable animal masquerades. We have just mentioned the weapons of the male animal, such as tusks, horns and antlers, which play a large part in mating time. In addition many animals have at their disposal a variety of attributes for attack and defence which help them in the struggle for existence— carapaces and shells, poisonous stings and fangs, a repulsive taste or odour, good powers of concealment, speed, skill or strength. Again, many animals possess none of these aids, or those they do possess are inadequate in the bitter struggle.

These weaklings have often been endowed with an entirely different form of protection. They are either inconspicuous or they imitate other better-protected animals. The Arctic zone and the desert afford classic examples of ordinary protective colouring. Here are to be found many animals whose white or yellowish colour conforms perfectly to the surroundings. This adaptability reaches a point where many animals, like the Arctic fox, the mountain hare and the ptarmigan, shed their useless winter garb when the snow melts in summer and don another more suited to the summer scene.

But we need not quote such extreme regions as the Arctic or the desert, for we can find the same principle at work in our meadows and woods. Frogs and lizards, as well as countless insects, are overlooked by their enemies on account of their green colouring. Butterflies, and in particular moths, protect themselves by imitating the greyish-brown hues of the bark when settled on trees. Hares, partridges and larks are magnificently adaptable in their colouring and in common with certain butterflies they use the well-known trick of feigning to be dead, or "freezing" in the right position. Spiders and beetles living on tree trunks are often only discovered when a piece of bark is ripped off and they are compelled to leave. Prior to this they could hardly be distinguished from the bark because of their superb camouflage. Some of our native caterpillars resort to amazing tricks: the caterpillar of the birch geometrid imitates a withered twig by raising its brown body rigidly in the air.

Recent research has shown that the caterpillars and pupæ of butterflies relate their camouflage to the pattern of light and shade on their bodies. The caterpillars choose their resting places so that their light bellies and dark backs assume the best possible position in relation to the light. If they are suddenly illuminated from the other side, they try to adopt a new position to achieve the right shadow distribution on their bodies. Many birds' eggs are ideally suited by their colour and pattern to the surroundings of the nest. The eggs of the golden plover closely resemble the pebbles of the seashore where the bird nests, and the green and brown spotted eggs of the lapwing assume the colours of the moor.

The mimicry practised by the grasshopper nymph is a common sight and the "wandering leaf", the hump-backed cricket, with its accurate imitation of the form and veins of a leaf, falls in the category of animal masquerades. These achievements are surpassed by certain butterflies from Java which imitate a leaf so accurately that even slight blemishes, fungoid spots, and withered parts appear on the wings. A certain projection of the lower wing gives the impression of the leaf stalk, a miracle of adaptation and one of the strange forgeries in Nature.

FORGERIES IN THE ANIMAL KINGDOM

Although those arts are surprising enough, even more curious things await us in this field. Not only are dead objects, such as leaves, branches, etc., imitated but also other animals. Besides protective colouring there is, as we know, its antithesis, the warning colour. Shrill colours, above all a combination of black, yellow or red, are used as a signal to warn possible "interested" parties of the poisonous nature or repulsive taste of the bearer. The salamander, with its poisonous epithelial glands and black and yellow marking, is as striking an example as our wasps, hornets, etc., with their flashy coloration. It is obvious that such warning colours possess a selective value in the Darwinian sense, for the wearers are in fact rarely importuned by enemies. The same device is also used by many other animals which, although they put on the same warning garb, are completely harmless!

Notable models are provided by the stinging bees and wasps. Surprisingly enough they are not only imitated by related species but also by butterflies, flies, beetles and grasshoppers. It would seem impossible that anyone could confuse a moth with a wasp, and yet this can happen in the case of the clear-wings (egeria) and the syrphid fly, which, in all the individual details of body outline, imitate the transparent wings of bees, bumblebees and wasps. Even their type of flight and their genuine-sounding "buzz" are reminiscent of their stinging models. The difference between flies and bees would seem unmistakable, but drone flies (eristalis), for example, are usually left alone by most people for fear of the presumed sting in what is in fact their leg. Ants again are faked by spiders, lice and beetles to good effect.

A particularly interesting case is provided by certain "guests" in the antheap. They cause great damage by stealing the eggs and the emmets and they can do this with impunity because, thanks to their mimicry, they are mistaken for their own kind by the genuine inhabitants of the nest. Oddly enough, this deception on the part of the "guest" conforms precisely to the capacities of the "hosts" in question. Ants, for example, which have well-developed eyes, will be imitated in colour and form, whereas blind ants are deceived by the form and hairy antennæ of the intruders.

The record is held by certain butterflies which, protected by their evil taste and warning colours, imitate other butterflies so successfully that even the practised entomologist finds it difficult to distinguish between the model and the fake. Many of these forgers have a special trick. There is, for example, an African swallowtail butterfly (*papilio dardanus*) whose males appear in a completely normal form, whereas the females are to be found in four different varieties. All four varieties of these metamorphosing females imitate protected models, but each a different one. They mimic the wings of their particular model, and it was by pure chance that naturalists were able to discover this fourfold imitation by one species. These females had previously been classified as four different species.

THE THEORY OF EVOLUTION—TODAY

Today we know for certain that life evolved from primitive stages to a multiplicity of forms and shapes. For their part these did not remain constant but, in the course of development, underwent countless transformations which began in the springtime of the earth and will presumably not end as long as our planet continues to support life. Darwin's reply to the question regarding the mechanics of evolution was the theory of natural selection, which has been confirmed on several counts and expanded by modern genetics. It has been proved that chemical and physical influences can bring about the sudden sharp changes in inheritance and mutations we have already described. Down the ages purely fortuitous changes of this nature could have brought advantages to certain individuals in the struggle for existence, which above all represents a conflict with environment.

This can easily be proved by a small calculation on the basis of an experiment carried out on fruit flies. It revealed that a gene mutation has a decisive effect if it gives its bearers an advantage of only 1%, and it appears only in one out of a thousand individuals. After 4,000 generations—not a particularly long span of time in hereditary terms—the mutated gene is still present in all the living individuals. In this way the new advantageous character has been fully established. But major changes, both small and large, are constantly taking place in all living creatures to a varying degree. For example, should climatic conditions change, there will always be individuals subject to mutation which will find it easier to adapt themselves to the changed living conditions. Such individuals and their issue will therefore be "selected", although the mutations in themselves may have been purely fortuitous and undirected.

Very important, too, are the advantages which can accrue to a living creature by mutation in its struggle with enemies. We have already mentioned that countless animals are well protected by skilful forms of camouflage, warning colours, etc., enabling them to establish favourable and effective tendencies in the struggle for existence. Those with striking colours are at the least advantage outside their natural surroundings. That very strange insect, the praying mantis, appears in several colours. If we confine a number of green mantises partly to green and partly to brown backgrounds, it will be found, after a short time, that nearly all the members of the second group are routed out by their enemies in the locality, whereas the well-camouflaged "prisoners" on the greenery have suffered practically no loss.

The natural "efficiency" of organisms subject to mutation can apply to the most diverse qualities. Thus adaptability may be more important than strength and dexterity, and powers of resistance to certain diseases or climatic effects of more importance than the powerful capacity to reproduce. Everything depends on the circumstances and the changes in question. In the case of primitive man, for example, physically powerful and agile individuals no doubt had better chances of survival than their weaker brothers. Different conditions of selection naturally apply in a "civilised" environment. According to a very interesting definition by Dobzhansky, it has become of decisive importance for modern man "to possess a nervous system which enables him to endure stress and to resist the wear and tear caused by the present-day tempo of life". It is probable that, in view of the long periods of time available for the development of living creatures, infinitesimal changes in the inheritance sufficed to achieve very important effects in the long run.

The "micro-evolution" caused by the smallest events in this domain can, in the course of millions of years, create the prequisites for "macro-evolution"—in other words, can lead to the creation of new species, genera and families. Time and time again purely fortuitous changes take place, most of them unfavourable or at least unimportant, but some of them, in the course of time and in different conditions, prove to be particularly favourable because they provide their bearers with a selection value in certain selective conditions. The various forms of mutation (*vide* section on inheritance) to a certain extent provide the "material" with which evolution works and lead to the selection of particularly suitable creations.

The theory of selection can incidentally provide an explanation why apparently negative characters, for instance the appearance of atrophied organs, are "justified" in certain circumstances. Most of the insects, including the butterflies, living on the Kerguelen Islands in the Indian Ocean have visibly stunted wings. There is a very illuminating reason for this. Since there is always a high wind blowing on these islands, the winged insects would be driven out to sea to their destruction. As a result of a mutation, insects evolved with stunted wings and consequently did not run the same risk; thus they could successfully survive in the struggle for existence—in their case the struggle with the wind. They survived not despite, but on account of, their defect and became the only representatives of the insects on these storm-tossed islands.

We must be wary of illusions in science and in particular in genetics, a subject which is as interesting as it is complex. The factors we have described certainly played a very great part in the development of life on earth, and still play their part today. But can the interpretations of the selection theory at our disposal, even in their most modern form, really answer all the questions? Research workers disagree on this issue. Some believe that the deductions we can make from the available evolutionary data are sufficient for us to understand the theory in its broad outlines. Other biologists are more sceptical. They do not deny, however, that the work on the solution of this problem, involving various disciplines from genetics to astrophysics, has led to great success.

The origin of new races and species has become comprehensible, but how can we account for the putative, almost revolutionary, change in the "dominant" living creatures? Why did the saurians die out comparatively quickly after they had conquered the greater part of the globe? And how can we explain the almost explosive development of the mammals as the successors of the saurians when they had already existed, although small and insignificant, millions of years before their rapid rise to power? Fossils prove moreover that other new forms of life appeared with surprising suddenness and in very great numbers. Can this really be explained by the long-term effect of the so-called micro-mutations? Or were there events in the nature of macro-mutations which at one blow accounted for a change in the former situation, producing completely new types? At the present moment we can give no answer to such questions. We know countless details of the development of life and its methodology, but the changes in its forms still pose unsolved problems.

The following question immediately arises. How was it possible for such marvellous organs as the eye of the vertebrate or the human brain to evolve by the interplay of undirected mutations? Or let us take an even simpler example, the mole's spade-hands. It is really hard to believe that such an uncommon foot, ideal for its purpose, could have developed by selection from purely fortuitous mutations. It must be added that any important change in the body of a living creature is conditional upon a wealth of further characters. Even if, in the case of the male, we accept a directed chain of mutations with a tendency to form spade-hands, countless other genes must have mutated in the "suitable" manner in order that the mole and not a monstrosity should be created. In its transition to life under the ground this animal must have had to develop many special features—a pointed head, a suitable form of body, smooth short-haired fur, etc.

Or to take a contrasting example, why did the mammoth possess such long and exaggeratedly curved tusks, and what was the point of the heavy antlers of the giant stag? Both of these creatures must have been at a disadvantage in the struggle for existence, and here we cannot really speak of a selection of particularly well-suited characters. There are an astonishing number of exceptions to the rules, which undoubtedly hold good in so many cases.

We are on the track of life and many of its long-guarded secrets can be solved by research. Nevertheless we must be modest in the face of Nature, which time and time again displays such an incredible faculty for creating new situations and satisfying the new needs of her living creatures. Doubtless in this respect "selection of the capable" plays a very great, if not decisive, role and it is certain that the struggle for existence signifies an effective control over the survival value of the mutations. But perhaps this only serves further to differentiate an already existing "basic type" of living creature. The types themselves could, in their formation, follow laws which we have not, or perhaps have only partially, recognised. Mutation and selection are so far the only proved factors in the morphology of living creatures, but that does not mean to say that other factors could not exist. Nature reveals an urge to develop, the effects of which we meet at every step in the infinite variety of life. Countless completely different species live side by side in the same regions, and all animals and plants have the capacity to react significantly and completely to the influences that concern them. For the moment this cannot be explained scientifically, for in biology we are constantly meeting barriers where concepts, such as usefulness or purpose, are no longer adequate. We can only continue to operate with more or less well-founded theories and at the same time be lost in wonder at the marvels of life.

THE PROBLEMS OF RELATIONSHIP

A woman standing outside the chimpanzees' cage at the zoo looked at the inmates behind the bars with obvious repugnance. "How can such things exist?" she said to one of the crowd. It was a classic remark, for here we find, in concrete form, an attitude which so many people feel, consciously or subconsciously, towards the problem of heredity. The well-known German biologist Professor Remane gives a very penetrating explanation of this observation of the woman outside the cage. "Chimpanzees," he says, "produce the effect of a human caricature, and many of us react with the typical expulsion reaction". We share this age-old tendency with many animals as a protest against any anomaly in members of our species. Among chickens a slight departure from the norm—for example, protruding primaries during the moult—can cause an attack by the others. The albino raven is persecuted by its black peers, and migratory birds incapable of flight are excluded. There are parallel cases in human beings. The physically or mentally deficient, such as cripples and idiots, can expect no compassion from children, for here too an expulsion reaction, which unconsciously determines the behaviour of children, is at work.

If an unscientific visitor to the zoo believes, entirely without justification, that science tries to claim the chimpanzee as one of our ancestors, then distaste turns to indignation. This was the first reaction of many really intelligent people to Darwin's theory when it was first published. When one of its most eager champions, T. H. Huxley, at a session of the British Society for the Promotion of Christian Knowledge, expounded such theses many of his audience were deeply insulted. At that famous

debate the malicious question was asked: was the speaker descended from the apes on his mother's or his father's side?
Naturally there was an uproar.

In actual fact Darwin never maintained that man is descended from the apes: he merely introduced his evolutionary
idea into biology. According to him—and on this score his
opinion is as modern as ever—there are certain affinities between the present-day primates and man himself. But it is a
very remote relationship, and thus it is a gross exaggeration to
describe the chimpanzee as our cousin, which was common in
those days. Actually, our biological connection with the chimpanzee lies in the fact that millions of years ago we had
common ancestors. These were the primates, which in the
course of the ages developed into two very different groups of
living creature—the Hominidæ (primitive and modern man)
on the one hand, and the Pongidæ (anthropoid apes) on the
other.

In the evolutionary line which led to man we can be quite
sure there never was a type that could serve as a model for the
present-day chimpanzee. This does not alter the fact that
Hominidæ and Pongidæ had a common basis. It is proved
by certain similarities in the molecular constitution of the
spermatozoa of man and the anthropoid apes. But in the last
analysis there are certain connections between ourselves and
any snake, for once upon a time mammals split away from the
reptile species. It is by no means paradoxical to go even further
back—to the cœlacanth, the first animal to climb out of the
sea on to the land. It too, then, can be counted among the
ancestors of the reptiles; and so, it would seem, we are also
related to fish.

No intelligent man today doubts the truth of the evolutionary theory, for somewhere and at some time development must
have started. In this connection it is immaterial whether we
take as our starting point the first protein molecule or some
animal ancestor. A far more important consideration is that
Darwin saw man far too one-sidedly as a creation among many
others, and the Haeckelian school saw our forefathers as primitive, brutal creatures which in their entire mode of behaviour
bore all the traits of the animal. Somewhere down the ages,
then, a gradual upward trend in man's development must have

taken place. He is therefore the end-product of a largely fortuitous process, whose methodology was natural selection in
the struggle for existence.

THE SPECIAL CASE OF MAN

In the meantime, however, particularly in recent times and
with the aid of completely new methods, countless proofs have
been forthcoming to show that the above viewpoint does not
hold good. It was a decisive mistake to equate the origin of
man, at least basically, with that of any other living creature,
for man is actually more than an animal and he has qualities
which give him a unique position among all the other creations of this earth. To begin with the negative side, according
to a definition by Professor Gehlen, man is an "imperfect being". He has no natural protection against the cold such as
animals have in the form of fur and feathers, and his physical
strength is insignificant compared with other animals the same
size as himself. A medium-sized dog has far better teeth than
his, and he lacks any real weapons, such as claws, tusk, etc. An
unarmed man is completely helpless when faced with a beast
of prey, and he can neither fight nor flee with any hope of success. He cannot even burrow unaided, for he has neither claws
nor the necessary muscular strength. Had such a creature remained purely animal in nature, it would soon have disappeared from the earth, because it was not equipped for the
stern struggle for existence.

That man, despite the physical defects we have mentioned,
became master of the earth means that his development must
have taken a different course from that which was formerly
accepted. Theodor Dobzhansky wrote:

> "Exclusively, or almost exclusively, human phenomena
> influence the biological solution of man so radically that it
> can hardly be understood unless one takes these things into
> account. On the other hand, human society and culture are
> the result of the biological evolution of our species. This
> means that the evolution of the human race is only compre-
> hensible as a result of the combination of biological and social
> forces."

Concepts such as "natural selection" and "the struggle for existence" alone will not carry us any further in our enquiry. Whether we speak in religious terms of a creative act of God or in purely scientific terms of a "great mutation", the event is unique for it has no parallel throughout the whole history of life on this planet. That is why it is so difficult to lay down a scientifically accurate basis of human origin, for the concepts used are either too ambiguous or too one-sided. This has constantly led to misunderstandings and marred all the arguments on the theory of evolution. The very term itself does not get to the root of the problem. In the case of man a precedent arose in the existing order, and this innovation is of sole importance. Evolution is therefore not actually the right word to use. Professor Lorenz, in a recent lecture, maintained that this applies to both the concepts "development" and "evolution". Neither of these words is entirely satisfactory. According to the professor the chicken may have developed from the egg, but man certainly did not "develop" from an ape-like creature. The very word is inadequate to express the decisive point: the origin of a living creature which, in good and evil, is distinguished from all the other creations. There is no appropriate word to denote the qualitative growth in the gradual higher development of man. Such difficulties in definition gave rise, in the course of discussions on this problem, to a host of different interpretations. Apes were looked upon as a kind of defective man or, more recently, man was seen as an "ape that had made the grade", although neither contention has anything to do with the true context of the evolutionary theory.

The French biologist, Jean Rostand, in his very readable book *The Adventure of Life*, summed it up in the following way:

"Man is undoubtedly descended from an animal resembling an ape. For it has been proved that in the past there were, on the one hand, apes which were far superior to present-day apes, and on the other hand men who were considerably lower than present-day man. These intermediate creatures, super-apes and sub-men, whose numbers are constantly increasing perpetually thanks to new palæontological discoveries, can be arranged in sequence. They make a very plausible ancestral portrait gallery—although it must be borne in mind that the relationship and evolutionary connections between these long-defunct creatures are purely hypothetical. In short, we know that they are related to each other, but we do not know whether it was a question of a great grandfather, a great uncle or even a very distant cousin. . . ."

This resumé is a trifle ironical and exaggerated, but it expresses the irrefutable fact that, in many respects, a number of lacunæ exist in our knowledge of the origins of man. The reason is mainly because there is a lack of reliable material. Easy though it was to reconstruct the development of the horse, it is a more difficult matter in the case of man. The forerunners of man existed some time in the Tertiary. But what did they look like, and which of them were the real ones? We can only determine this, more or less, from the few bones and teeth which are dug up here and there, dispersed over large areas of the globe. We have no complete skeleton of an ape from those far-distant periods, and so far not a single skeleton of a human forerunner.

Nature obviously carried out a host of experiments, successful and unsuccessful, in the creation of man. There were the most disparate intermediate forms, and it is often uncommonly difficult to say whether the living creature under discussion was still an animal or already a man. As usual, Nature, in this her most important experiment, took her time and explored all the possibilities. There was every conceivable intermediate stage and branch route on the way to man, and often enough the result was "unsatisfactory". Groups of men-like creatures died out, only to be replaced by something better.

HOW DID MAN ORIGINATE?

From the bases we have outlined the question cannot be answered with certainty, but the development can at least be observed in its broad outlines. As we have seen, an almost explosive development of mammals took place in the Tertiary. At that time, too, those forms were created from which the Hominidæ (primitive and modern men) and Pongidæ (anthropoid apes) were descended. About 30 million years ago lived a creature whose remains were discovered near Lake Victoria in

East Africa. At first it was believed to be a primitive chimpanzee, and the find (the remains of a jaw with teeth) was named "Proconsul" after a living chimpanzee called Consul. A little later this conjecture was proved wrong, for presumably the Proconsuls stood at the beginning of a million-year development which led in one line to the primates and in the other line to man.

It is completely out of the question that between Proconsul and the first proto-human forms there was a type which could serve as a model for the present-day chimpanzee. The Proconsuls moved just as easily on the ground as in the trees, proving that they were not yet specialised. About 10 million years ago, then, as finds in Italy proved, a mountain ape appeared called *Oreopithecus bambolii*, which already shows a certain advance in the direction of the Hominidæ. Whether it is to be considered as one of our ancestors or only a specimen of a branch, a model which was abandoned, is a matter of controversy. In any case, this creature already displayed signs of an adaptation to life on the ground and also to an upright gait.

Further development led to countless intermediate stages, all of which we do not know about. During the Ice Age, in the so-called "animal-man-transition stage", new forms arose which represent experiments with the new creature to be—man. *Australopithecus* appeared about a million years ago, a sideline which did not lead to man but which bore a tendency towards such a line. *Australopithecus* shows a certain resemblance to the chimpanzee but is nearer to man because he walked upright and contrived to polish bones and use them as tools.

There are several further proofs of the intensity with which the development towards man took place in all possible directions during the Ice Age. We have *Pithecanthropus Erectus*, the assumed forerunner of man, which the Dutch palæontologist Dubois found in Java. Dubois went there in search of the famous missing link—the link between man and ape. By an extraordinary stoke of luck he found the remains of just such a creature, but today we know that several such intermediate and transitional forms existed. *Sinanthropus*, to name one, like *Pithecanthropus*, knew fire and primitive tools. Closely related to him is the famous Heidelberg Man, the oldest European fossil man, whose lower jaw was found near Heidelberg in 1907.

Countless further finds fill in the picture down to Neanderthal Man, who lived mainly as a hunter and hoarder. Neanderthal Man, Ngandong Man from Java and Broken Hill Man from Rhodesia show many individual differences, but we can observe here, in the main line, an important further development of primitive man. In the course of the Palæolithic his tools and stone weapons became more useful and efficient, and this development lasted until the middle of the last Ice Age, when it came to an abrupt end. Neanderthal Man disappeared without a trace. Perhaps he died out, or maybe his successor routed him out. We cannot tell.

The successor was a far more perfect creature than all the forerunners. He was *Homo Sapiens*, modern man, who looked very different from the clumsy Neanderthal man. He was slimmer and taller, dolichocephalic, with a high forehead and well-defined chin. It is a very remarkable fact that *Homo Sapiens* appeared almost simultaneously and unheralded in Europe, Africa, Asia, and Australia. Two European races have been named after the sites of their discovery in France—Cro-Magnon Man and Aurignac Man. There is much to favour the theory that the former played the deciding role. Incidentally, Cro-Magnon Man appears to be older than was at first thought, and it is quite possible that he existed before Neanderthal Man. In any case, we are faced once more with the fact that a completely new type, in this instance the highest type of all, displays an astonishingly swift development. From the first Primates to *Pithecanthropus* at least 60 million years elapsed, but from the latter to the appearance of modern man only half a million!

Many finds show that with the appearance of *Homo Sapiens diluvialis* a completely new phase began, for this being no longer lived as his forefathers had done, struggling exclusively for survival: he rose above it and discovered art, jewellery and possibly the myth. For the first time an inhabitant appeared on the earth who wished to be more than a "bit of Nature". And now, slowly, the flower of creation, cultivated humanity, began to open. Artfully fashioned tools and ornamented utensils appeared, and astonishingly true-to-life drawings adorned the walls of his caves. Man produced the first sculptures and began to use bones and antlers as working materials. He also started to bury his dead.

WHY DID MAN BECOME MASTER OF THE EARTH?

In all probability the environment of man-in-the-making was a treeless steppe. His ancestors must have given up living in trees, and his new way of life compelled him to adopt first a semi-upright and finally a completely upright bearing, whereby his head and hands were anatomically favoured for further high development. That development of the brain began which we can observe to some extent by an increase in cranial content. In primitive man the cranial capacity is between 900 and 1,100 cu.cm., in Neanderthal Man about 1,200 cu.cm., and in modern man about 1,500 cu.cm. (the present-day chimpanzee, on the other hand, has a cranial content of 350–480 cu.cm.). Qualitative rather than quantitative increase of the brain was naturally of greater significance. In addition to his vitally important speech, man acquired the power to reason, a capacity beyond even the most developed animals. Just as important as thought for man's advance was undoubtedly his conscious behaviour, which is recognisable in his very early use of tools. In his hands primitive man had at his disposal the best natural tools that exist on earth. In the hand his whole activity was concentrated in a decisive manner.

Future man, thanks to his "thinking hand", was able to make tools and weapons. Fashioned flints and various primitive tools were found among the earliest human remains. *Homo erectus*, the creative animal, at the first glimmer of conscious thought, had in the hand a means of translating thought into action. Countless examples of unsuccessful and rejected objects of primitive man show clearly enough how difficult and tiring the beginnings of thinking action must have been. But the final separation from the animal took place with the first self-made tool; a technique was discovered and the path taken which finally made man the master of creation. But an animal can also use tools. It will smash a fruit on a stone, and apes, for example, know how to use poles and crates to reach food which is placed out of reach. But there is a fundamental difference: the animal uses tools whereas man creates them, thanks to his thinking hand. Even today, in many of our everyday tools (consider the hammer and pincers) we can see that the hand served as the model. In the course of his development man's ingenuity increased; he emerged from the darkness of animal life and began to work with his hands in his mighty struggle with Nature. The results of his efforts finally justified his calling his own comparatively short history "world history".

CHAPTER V

The Multiformity of Life

OBVIOUSLY a very long time elapsed before science acquired a fairly complete overall picture of all the species of the larger animals because of the infinite variety of life on earth. This applies, of course, only to the animals that live on the earth today and not to their forerunners, many of which are completely unknown. To begin with, small living creatures from earlier ages could not usually be found with the normal methods used by "fossil collectors". In recent times, however, new techniques have been developed in palæontology and they have brought surprising results. Let us quote a practical example. Dr. A. Cooper of the American National Museum, with the help of weak organic acids, dissolved a 200-million-year-old stratum of rock from Texas weighing about 30 tons. His gigantic task proved worth while, for in this particular rock fossils of more than 3 million primitive living creatures were discovered.

They consisted in the main of snails, mussels, corals and other tiny creatures of which very little had been known previously. In another instance small chalk deposits dating from the Tertiary were subjected to the same treatment. The result? A host of insects from that remote past, some of whose internal organs were in a better state of preservation than those of the famous fauna imprisoned in amber. Furthermore, fish eggs, insect larvæ, hairs of mammals, algæ and even bacteria from the Tertiary were discovered. This was only a start, but it proved what a wealth of life can be contained even in rock horizons which had previously been considered poor in fossils.

Such surprises are often in store for the palæontologist, but in the last analysis he is only concerned, so to speak, with the legacy of life from former periods. How does our taxonomy look today? Are we familiar with all the living creatures that inhabit the earth? The answer can only be in the negative if we are to be honest. Naturally differences arise according to the phylum under consideration. We can rest assured that no surprises are in store for us in the case of land vertebrates, but without question we know only a proportion of the insects and molluscs living on the earth today. And, when we come to the great host of protozoa, we can safely say that the next pond will probably produce countless forms that have never yet been classified. Nevertheless our catalogue of animal species has made good progress since the days of Linnaeus. When he compiled his system of the animal kingdom only 4,286 species were known. A hundred years later the number had risen to about 88,000. Today we know more than a million, and new species are being discovered every year.

THE AGE OF THE INSECTS

Short-lived man, whose race is the most recent of all, proudly terms himself the "master of the earth" and undoubtedly has good grounds for this claim. Nevertheless one of the greatest modern entomologists, Professor L. Howard, once made the paradoxical statement that we are not actually living in the age of man but in the age of the insect. Naturally he did not mean this to be taken seriously, but there is a grain of truth in his utterance. It is a fact that today the insects represent the greatest proportion of all the animal inhabitants of the earth. The ruling dynasty of vertebrates embraces about 66,000 species, of which 7,000 fall into the category of mammals. There are 20,000 known species of birds and 22,000 species of fish. As opposed to these comparatively low figures, the insects lead the field with more than 600,000 species so far recorded. This figure is still probably too low, and biologists consider it possible that there are more than a million species of insects living on our planet.

Down the ages the insects developed a wealth of forms and characters which enabled them to survive all the earth's catastrophes and all attacks from their enemies. We find insects in the tropics and in the Arctic Circle; they live in the water, the air and the earth, in compost heaps and even in petroleum. They are ubiquitous. Wherever the slightest possibility for life exists they are to be found, and they eat everything apart from glass and iron.

Insects are by no means lower forms of life and in their 300-

million-year evolution they have withstood all the vicissitudes
of destiny and climatic changes to a remarkable degree. Many
of them still look very much like their forebears from the
Carboniferous, so efficiently was their internal organisation
prepared for any emergencies. Others have changed considerably, and in the earth's history countless new species have
evolved which, with regard to the quality of their organs, can
compete with the highly developed vertebrates.

We know that living creatures can adapt themselves to
changes in living conditions, climatic or otherwise, by a selection of those mutations which happen to be particularly suited
to the demands made upon them. In the case of insects their
swift sequence of generations afforded many more mutations
than were possible in the case of long-living creatures. This
was naturally an advantage. Incidentally, one fact gives us
cause for reflection in our atomic age: insects have a far greater
resistance to radiation than any mammal and they could
therefore withstand the results of an inconceivably vast catastrophe unleashed by man—a nuclear war. Thus a situation is
conceivable in which the insects might not only be numerically,
as before, but actually the masters of the earth. Professor von
Frisch points out in this connection that man's rulership rests
on his intelligence, but intelligent men often realise too late
how unintelligent their thoughts have been.

Compared with their bodily weight, insects have a small,
barely qualified brain. It is certainly not capable of reflection.
In spite of this they are capable of astonishing achievements of
the most involved nature, nothing comparable being found anywhere else in the animal kingdom. How is it possible? It is a
question of particularly well-developed instincts which have
been passed down from generation to generation from time
immemorial. They regulate all the vital behaviour patterns
of these creatures on a comparatively simple principle. Everything follows in a prescribed manner. The rule alone is worthy
of consideration, and exceptions are "invalid". (When these
occur and the insect is faced with an unusual task it nearly
always fails.) But in practice such exceptions are rarely found
and the predetermined achievements, thanks to the reliable
regulation of their course, are usually fulfilled one hundred per
cent.

The "construction details" of these animals are really astonishing and should fill our engineers with envy. Even the smallest insect—a parasitic wasp of the *mymaridæ* family measuring 0·21 mm.—has at its disposal a host of muscles, joints, complicated organs, etc., all of which function perfectly, although it has no bone structure. The skeleton of an insect is its skin, which is composed of a remarkably efficient material—chitin. One has only to pick up a beetle to notice the "technical qualities" of such an organism. The carapace is very resistant and at the same time relatively light; the legs are so stable that their bearing-power is unrivalled in the animal kingdom. A scarab, for example, was loaded with small weights until it was proved that this insect could carry 850 times its own bodily weight. (The average man can carry hardly two-thirds of his own weight.)

The lightly built mosquito cheerfully imbibes so much blood that the "burden" corresponds to double its own bodily weight. In spite of this it flies as well as ever with about 300 wing beats per second. Dragonflies with their delicate wings are capable of the fantastic speed of 40 m.p.h., and even butterflies indulge in migrations that take them thousands of miles. Painted ladies (*vanessa cardui*), marked with dye, have proved that they have covered the enormous stretch from North Africa to Iceland.

The toughness of such insects is in many cases scarcely conceivable. It has often been observed that caterpillars, when wounded at one end of the body, will begin to devour themselves. From such observations it has been concluded that insects do not feel pain. Professor von Frisch quotes the following example in point: if, with a pair of scissors, one cuts the abdomen from the thorax of a bee while it is drinking sugared water, the insect usually continues with its meal as though nothing had happened. The liquid naturally runs out of the severed body, but the victim continues to drink until it falls dead. The presumed absence of pain is logical enough, for the chitin carapace of insects is so stable that, as opposed to our sensitive skin, there is no need for the alarm system of pain. On the other hand, a special problem is posed by the growth of the insect in its carapace. Since the latter is rigid, growing insects require a new covering from time to time. The old one breaks open and the insect, in the truest sense of the saying, "jumps out of its skin". During the short time that it is without the protective chitin covering the body has an opportunity of expanding until the new carapace hardens. The expansion process is often hastened by an intake of air or water so that it can proceed without delay.

These are but a few examples of the distinguishing features in the body-building of insects, but they have another quality which has been a decisive factor in their survival since the beginnings of time. It is their enormous procreative power. Theoretically a single housefly can produce a billion progeny in a few months, and it has been calculated that a plant-louse whose issue could procreate without loss would, in a short summer, breed so many children and grand-children that their weight would amount to more than 10 billion tons. But Nature has seen to it that trees never reach the sky. All these figures are purely theoretical and in practice, out of 100 eggs from a pair of flies, an average of 98 die before sexual maturity. The same applies to other insects. Nevertheless they are still man's most serious rivals because, thanks to their versatility and number, they continue to dispute with him for the rulership of the earth. They carry serious diseases such as malaria, yellow fever, etc.; they kill his domestic animals and consequently make large tropical areas almost uninhabitable; they destroy the harvests of his fields and vineyards, thus causing him enormous expense in combating them, and in spite of all the progress in insecticides, etc., that expense is often in vain.

On the other hand, many insects are not only useful but almost vital, because they carry out the pollination of beneficial plants. One has only to quote the industrious bees, with which we simply could not dispense—not to mention their honey. A single bee can visit 30 to 40 flowers in the course of a minute. If for some reason the number of these insects were to diminish, the harvests of important plants, and above all of fruit trees, would decline in a very short space of time. Let us therefore now consider the bee, one of our most interesting insects on account of its astonishing achievements.

Among bees, bumblebees, wasps and ants a "community sense" rules far surpassing anything man can achieve, and we are therefore justified in speaking of insect states. They are the oldest states in the world because they were in existence at a period in the earth's history before even the elementary pre-stages of man, not to allude to any human society. Admittedly the community-forming insects, in all their activities, only follow the rigid laws of their inherited instincts, but the latter lead to such astonishingly "intelligent" and practical behaviour that man has always been fascinated by these remarkable states and their customs. The best-known is the bee community, for the honey-bee has long since become one of our "domestic animals". Among bees there is no egoism, only the interest of the state in the best sense; the well-being of the community is inherent in all their activities. The working population consists of females which have renounced their reproductive function. The queen mother of the hive is the only one capable of procreation, and she makes good use of this privilege by laying more than 1,000 eggs daily. The male drones are tolerated in the hive only until they have fertilised the queen, when they are sacrificed as superfluous and die of hunger or from the poisonous sting of a worker bee.

Each worker bee must fulfil a number of tasks in a prescribed sequence during its life, and naturalists, as a result of prolonged observation, are well-informed about their "curriculum". The first three days are devoted to cleaning the cells, the following days to the feeding of the old brood with pollen and honey. The young brood cannot yet digest this solid nourishment and have to be satisfied with a nutritious juice which the workers excrete from their salivary glands. From the sixth day onwards the young nurse is in a position to produce this necessary "mother's milk". Until the tenth day she continues with her task but has a number of additional duties, such as cleaning the larvæ and helping them to hatch. Since the temperature in the hive must be kept at about 95° F, the nurse sits closely pressed to the cell as a living oven during cold weather.

Towards the end of this nursing period the worker trains for her "foreign service" by making practice reconnaissance flights near the hive. At times she will still be employed in the hive, in particular in building, for the worker bee has begun to excrete wax instead of the fodder juice, which has now dried up. She kneads the wax into lumps for the building of the nurseries and larders and she does this so efficiently that, according to mathematical calculations, no better employment of space and material is possible. Nevertheless this astonishing architecture is only a sideline, for her major work during this period (tenth to eighteenth day) is the unloading of the nectar brought in by the collectors and its transport to the cells. At the same time there is the daily cleaning work, for the hive must always be kept clear of all refuse. Now her flights grow longer, but no nectar is brought back. Before she is allowed to embark on this task the bee must spend a few days on watch. On the twentieth day she at last becomes a collector and brings back pollen, clinging to her legs like "trousers", and honey in her honeybag, the contents of which she regurgitates in the hive.

This industrious creature now has but a short time to live—unless she happens to be a bee that hatched out in the autumn. In this event she lives through the winter and has an easy time for several months, because the queen lays no eggs during the cold season. In the spring the hive divides: it "swarms". The old queen leaves with half her subjects to look for a new home, and a young queen's reign begins. She has matured in a brood cell larger than the others and, as a result of special nourishment ("royal jelly"), is fully developed and nubile, whereas the worker bees, having been under-nourished as larvæ, have atrophied ovaries.

This is a brief survey of some of the achievements of the industrious bees made possible by their highly developed instincts. They also possess sense organs which are surprisingly well developed for an insect. Honey-bees distinguish most flowers by their colour and scent, and they can find their bearings even in the dark hive. Their fine sense of taste is difficult to deceive, as experiment has shown. Sweet but sugarless saccharine is rejected out of hand. A remarkably well-developed "memory" enables the small collectors to find their way back from the flowers they have visited several miles away.

This acuteness of the senses explains many of the bee's amazing achievements, but not the most important feature of their community life—co-operation for a common purpose. Only when there is an understanding between animals—as occurs in the hive—can such co-operation exist. When a bee has found a rich source of nectar she flies wildly in circles round the hive, thus alerting the other collectors. They recognise the goal, the plant in question, from the scent which clings to the body of the scout, but how will they discover the direction of this goal? Here we have *in petto* a problem we will meet with again in bird migration. In recent times it has been satisfactorily solved, thanks to the biologist von Frisch, who has conducted exhaustive experiments to unravel the secrets of "bee language". We cannot go into full detail here, and must confine ourselves to a sketch of his most important findings. They are surprising enough in themselves, for they show instinctive achievements on the part of the bees which far surpass anything we previously suspected about them.

Von Frisch used hives with a glass window, through which he could watch his experimental insects. He then arranged sources of food at different distances from the hive. These consisted of bowls of sugared water standing on pieces of cardboard sprayed with suitable essences such as lavender oil, etc.—typical and easily recognisable scents for the bees. By the systematic removal of the bowls the bees were slowly enticed further and further away from the hive, to their potential limit. It now remained to be proved how the discoverer would be able to direct her colleagues to the food sources.

The news is given by dances performed by the bees on the comb—in the case of nearby sources of food by round dances (tripping in a circle), and in the case of supplies at a long distance by "tail-wagging" dances (wriggling movements of the abdomen). These dances were closely observed and recorded. It was found that on a horizontal surface the direction of the food source could be given by the dance direct. If the hive were turned on its plane, then the dancing bee functioned like a compass, and continued to take up its position in the appropriate direction. The same principle was followed when the dances took place on a horizontal take-off board at the entrance to the hive. But since the scouts usually dance on the vertical honeycomb, how can they give the right direction in these conditions? This too was discovered. They take the angle formed by the flight to the source of the food and the position of the sun, and transpose this angle to the direction of gravity. Certain differences in the rhythm of the tail-wagging dances give the inmates of the hive further information regarding the distance from their goal. For nearer distances the round dance gives the information that the food, whose perfume the dancing bee carries, is to be looked for within a radius of about 85 yards. The actual direction only follows in distances over 85 yards, when not only the distance itself but the prevailing wind is taken into account. A contrary wind increases and a tail wind decreases the figure of distance. This is particularly illuminating biologically, for the bees are able to glean from the information how much time and energy are needed to reach the signalled goal. The vital issue is that bees not only adhere rigidly to the given direction but can find their bearings by the position of the sun, even when the latter is hidden by cloud.

How do they accomplish this amazing feat? There was no satisfactory answer until Professor von Frisch and his colleagues put them to the test in a very interesting experiment carried out in the summer of 1959. Von Frisch's suspicion that there is a "bee language" was confirmed. The bees find their direction from the ultra-violet radiation of the sun which, as we know, is invisible to the human eye. The experimental hive with the glass window was placed on the roof of the Munich Observatory, laid flat in this case so that the bees could give the direction of the sun direct by their tail-wagging dances. Some of the bees were marked with dye spots, an artificial feeding ground was arranged, and now it only remained to be seen how they would inform their fellow hive-dwellers on their return. The experiments were carried out under a covered sky. It was found that the path-finding dances beneath a densely covered sky (heavy rainclouds) were disorientated and led to no bearing being given.

The situation was quite different when the sun, covered by a thin layer of cloud, was invisible to the human eye but still recognisable within the range of ultra-violet light. This light is particularly intense and has its own "colour quality" for bees, whereas it does not register on the human retina. It now had to be verified whether the marked bees, with their tail-wagging dances, really would record the exact position of the sun. On their return their dances were observed through the glass pane and they registered the precise direction. At the same time the sun was photographed through the observatory telescope with infra-red plates. The results of the exposures were compared with the "reports" of the dancing bees to corroborate their reliability.

This interesting experiment was a complete success and showed how ultra-sensitive bees are to the least changes in light. The infra-red photographs revealed that the brightness of the clouded sky at the actual position of the sun was 5% more intense than that of the remaining cloud cover—a very small difference, but it was quite enough for the bees' eyes. In every case they knew the exact position of the sun and gave it in their dances because they could see the sun through the clouds. During the whole series of the tests the sun was never visible to any of the scientists taking part.

ACCOMPLISHMENTS AND VICES OF THE ANTS

Despite the truly remarkable achievements described above, it would be quite wrong to endow insects with intelligent behaviour in the human sense. Even the most complicated behaviour of bees derives from fundamental instincts from which they are incapable of deviating in the slightest. Ants are more "intelligent", and by this, of course, we mean adaptable, as can be recognised immediately by their building methods. According to the need and the occasion, they use all types of material for their great variety of nests. There are the earth nests, which consist of a labyrinth of chambers and corridors, sometimes completely underground and sometimes under stones or roofed over with great heaps of soil. There are mud nests in trees, which means that all the material has to be laboriously carried aloft. For reinforcing these "ant gardens" the roots of certain plants, sown by the ants themselves for the purpose, are used. The surface parts of these nests are often buttressed with grass stalks and other plant components, or with little stones.

The "upper works" are important to the nest for two reasons: they regulate the outflow of rain water and serve as heating for the whole edifice. Thanks to the stones and the mound of earth, the upper stories of the nest are warmed by the sun while the lower remain cool. These differences in temperature are necessary in the interest of the brood, for the larvæ need different degrees of warmth according to their age. For this reason they are carried about the nest by the workers as and when necessary. The large antheaps in our forests are covered over with pine needles and other vegetable material to provide this "central heating", the actual nest being in the soil beneath. According to the latest measurements, the temperature inside these nests exceeds the outdoor temperature by 50° to 59° F. Many types of ants build "wooden nests", with countless corridors and chambers, which they burrow out of rotting tree trunks. Many tropical ants use wood for the so-called "carton" nests; they chew it into pulp and cement it with a glutinous glandular secretion.

The greatest perfection in nest building among ants—in fact among all insects in the world—is achieved by the weaver ants. They build in the foliage of living trees and bushes, using the leaves, which they bind together with a web, as walls. For a long time it was difficult to see how they achieved this, for the ants have no glands which could produce any web secretion. The solution was eventually found, and it proved surprising. The larvæ of this species are equipped with large spinning-glands, although they are not able of their own accord to participate in the work. But the workers know how to exploit them. They hold the leaves together and compel the larvæ, with gentle pressure, to do the binding with the aid of their spinning-glands. A host of ants, each one carrying a larva in its jaws, press the heads of their victims firmly to the edge of a leaf until the liquid is secreted; the performance is then repeated on the edge of the neighbouring leaf, until the gulf between the two leaves is finally filled with a fine criss-cross web. The living tool has completed its task.

A mode of life disastrous to mankind is found among the leaf-cutting ants of South and Central America. They build gigantic earth nests descending to a depth of 30 feet, where they prepare their own food—self-cultivated fungi—in the numerous chambers. Tiny pieces cut from the leaves of plants are carried into the nest to serve as a compost for the fungi. No one would worry but for the fact that the ants need a fantastic number of leaves for their fungus plantations, and these, of course, are often the leaves of our cultivated plants. The ants launch a full-scale invasion, and so far all attempts to control their depredations have been in vain. To dig out the deep nests is very laborious and, in view of their number, very costly; furthermore it is impossible to tell whether one corner of the building has not remained intact, from which a whole new colony will be born in a very short space of time. The use of poison is unrewarding, for the insects will eat nothing but their self-grown fungi. Attempts have been made to smoke out the nests with chemicals, or to destroy them by flooding, but this, too, proved of little avail, because the vast expanse of the edifice prevented its being completely destroyed. For the moment, therefore, man is completely powerless in the face of the small leaf-cutting ants and must look on while whole acres of his best farmland are destroyed and rendered useless. In the state of São Paulo, in Brazil, damage amounting annually to a sum of over four million pounds is caused in this way.

Incidentally, these leaf-cutting ants are the only pure vegetarians among the formicoidea. All other species have a far more varied menu. In their ceaseless hunt for caterpillars and other vermin they are very useful in our forests, and last but not least they shine as real paragons of industry! This good reputation cannot be applied to all species of ants, for many of them indulge in a variety of vices. There are the robber ants, tiny creatures which live in the nests of their larger relations: they dig their own small corridors, down which their hosts cannot follow them, and wreak havoc among the stores of food and the defenceless brood.

Other species are no less parasitic. They keep slaves, usually members of a weaker species, captured as larvæ and which then have to work for their masters. Such indolence can lead to the point where the Amazon ants, for example, are no longer capable of doing any real work. Without the help of their slaves they would starve, for they cannot even eat unaided. They never try to take their own nourishment but give orders in their "feeler speech" to their slaves to feed them. And for some strange reason the slaves do as they are bid. After a time the Amazon ants go "slaving" once more, attack foreign ants' nests, and thus ensure the future of their far from industrious existence.

The principle of camouflage is used successfully by a great many animals. A good example is that of young snipe, whose admirably protective coloring makes them very difficult to see on the ground.

Below: Another method of protection for an animal is to remain motionless. A toad freezes at the appearance of a snake and stays unharmed, because the enemy completely overlooks its motionless prey.

Insects are particularly talented in the art of camouflage. They imitate leaves, stalks and lichen, foliage, and moss, in color and aspect.

Left: Stick insects resemble small twigs.

Right: The caterpillar of the lappet moth.
(*Gastropacha quercifolia.*)

The pupa of the swallowtail butterfly conforms aptly to its surroundings.

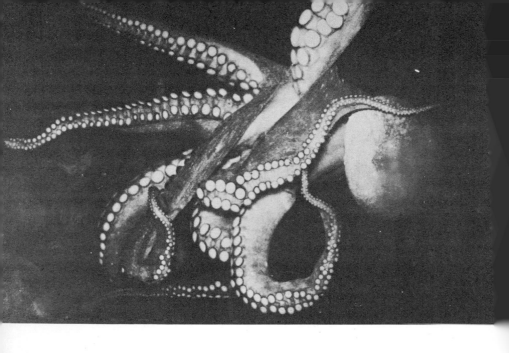

It is misleading to call the octopus a fish, because it is in fact a mollusc. When in danger it ejects a "smoke cloud" of inky black fluid to aid its escape. These creatures are remarkably speedy in attack and in flight.

It is well known that certain species indulge in a kind of cattle-breeding, and that aphids in the main are kept as domestic animals. They are much loved by the ants on account of the sweet excretion, known as "honeydew", which they release when their bellies are stroked. A less well-known fact, which has been observed on numerous occasions, is that the ants sometimes succumb to drunkenness. In exchange for the succulent juice they abandon their legendary industry and give up all other duties, even the feeding of their own larvæ. Only their drink-providing guests are carefully tended, until the ants, victims of their vice, do not even bother to go out and look for food; finally the colony dies out.

MULTIFORMITY OF INSTINCTS

Insects are ideally suited to research into the problem of instinct, for their achievements in this respect are highly varied and impressive. The "intelligence" of bees and ants has become a byword, but actually intelligence does not come into the picture because they behave entirely by instinct. Instinct exists in many shapes and forms, from the simplest to the most complicated. Let us take as our example the very striking case of the yucca moth (*tegeticula yuccasella*). This small creature lays its eggs in the ovaries of the yucca blossom, on whose seed the caterpillars then feed. Once a female emerges from its cocoon, it flies immediately after mating to a yucca blossom, removes some pollen from the anthers and rolls it into a little ball. Thus laden the insect goes to a second blossom and does something quite different. With its ovipostor it pierces the stigma, lays a number of eggs, and then closes the opening with the small ball of the pollen it has collected. In this way the yucca moth, in the most subtle way, has provided for her young. The pollen conveyed fertilises the yucca, so that it can produce further seeds to be used as food.

The number of the eggs laid is so moderate that the caterpillars have enough to eat until pupation, and there is still seed to spare. Thus the plant also gains, for without the interference of this small moth it would presumably remain barren. But did this creature behave intelligently? The reply is unfortunately "No". The yucca moth never knew its parents, so there is no question of learning from experience. Inherited instinct alone rules her behaviour in the interest of the preservation of the species, and this is the case with countless other instincts which we shall meet with in the realm of the rearing of young.

It sometimes happens that in changed conditions the normal instinctive behaviour does not lead to its goal, and perhaps a change of procedure could have a better effect. How does the animal then behave, and does it alter the instinctive pattern?

Biology knows countless cases where such a change does not necessarily do immediate damage to the animal, even though it may lead to absurdity and even to degeneration. This can easily be proved. A zoologist, for example, watched members of an ant community which normally carry the waste matter from the nest to special "middens" some distance away. They had, for some reason, settled in the crevices of a wall, and the simplest thing would have been to let the detritus fall direct from the nest entrance, but in no single instance did this occur. With touching diligence the ants carried their burden to the predetermined distance from the nest entrance before dumping the rubbish, which naturally fell to the ground, as it would have done from the nest itself.

Another example is quoted by Fabre, the father of entomology. On one of his walks he came across a train of caterpillars of the processionary moth (*thaumetopœa pityocampa*), which assemble in huge numbers and travel linked together by a silken thread. Fabre attached the leader of the column to the rear member. The caterpillars continued to play follow my leader and circled for seven days without noticing that anything was amiss.

Very rewarding attempts in this direction have also been made with digger wasps (*ammophila sabulosa*). A certain species has the habit of slipping into its nest on arrival in order to check that all is well, leaving whatever booty it has brought home outside the entrance. An observer removed this booty from one of the wasps and laid it a short distance from the entrance. The owner returned after its tour of inspection, started a feverish search and soon found what it had lost. Before re-entering the wasp dropped it once more and slipped unloaded into the nest as usual. When it came out for the second time the booty had again disappeared, and the same performance was repeated more than forty times without the wasp once entertaining the idea that it could carry its prey directly into the nest. Such examples can be quoted *ad infinitum*, but each case shows clearly that, often enough, no experience can induce animals to work in any other way than according to their deeply ingrained instincts.

However, we should not conclude from these facts that instinct functions only along a single track. According to their level of organisation and the circumstances, animals can vary their instinctive behaviour within certain bounds providing— as opposed to the above illustrations—it has not been too firmly entrenched. Thus birds in general build their nests in a predetermined manner, but they can use different materials. Again, the small larva of our European caddis fly is capable of such variation. It normally builds a protective shelter of tiny stones, but given other building materials it will use them for the same purpose. When there is too little material it works very economically. Instinct is not utterly blind and can be corrected by experience: very often a combination of instinct and the capacity to learn is vital for an animal. A newly hatched chick starts pecking at small ears of corn by instinct, but it often misses the grain and only after three weeks can it register an average of 80% of "hits".

What of the stupidities we have quoted in the above cases resulting from a close adherence to instinct? They are really no proof against the mutual support of instinct and experience. The latter is only possible in an environment determined by the natural living conditions of the animal. Without human intervention it would hardly occur that in a train of processionaries the leader would suddenly make for the rear member; and by teasing the digger wasp an artificial change from the normal course of events was created. We should not attribute to instinct more than it can achieve. A human being suddenly set down on Mars, despite his intelligence, would presumably not behave in a purely rational manner either.

ANIMALS ARE DIFFERENT

As opposed to men, animals react to any given situation in their environment exclusively with pre-determined reactions peculiar to their species. The larger part of these are innate, while others have to be learned. Very young animals can indulge in certain forms of behaviour without any practice. For instance, it is vital for nestlings to make themselves "invisible" immediately a bird of prey flies above them. They possess therefore an instinct which warns them of their enemies. If we place a cut-out showing the outlines of a bird of prey above a nest containing young, the little ones immediately duck and try to hide themselves. They do this invariably, even if they have never seen a bird of prey before, because they already carry its picture in themselves as soon as they come out of the egg. The pattern "bird of prey" is given accurately by instinct, distinguishing it from other harmless birds. Experiments showed quite clearly that the cut-out of a dove or some equally innocuous bird evoked no such ducking reaction when held over the nest.

Newly hatched chicks will peck at corn, an item they already "knew about" in the egg. Singing birds, experimentally confined to soundproof rooms, can sing various passages of their natural song without any previous practice. Other abilities, on the contrary, needed certain training. Ravens, for instance, know by instinct the motions of nest-building, but they must learn first of all what materials to use. Young squirrels know how to open nuts, but they only learn by trial and error that there are various methods.

A very interesting discovery in modern research into behaviourism is afforded by a factor known as "identification". The well-known animal psychologist, Professor Lorenz, once had a remarkable experience of this. He had placed the eggs of a wild goose in an incubator in order to watch the chicks hatch out. When the first shell burst open the little creature caught sight of the man and immediately identified him as the mother. It ran behind the professor and refused most energetically to remain with the farmyard goose which had been chosen as fostermother. Normally the mother is the first living creature with whom the young come in contact. Their identification instinct tells them that they must follow her, hence the mistake of our gosling is easily explained.

Young dogs will lie on their backs when confronted by a more powerful rival, and in a fight crows will offer the victor the most sensitive parts of their necks; upon this the contest ends immediately. We know today that beasts of prey in particular, and incidentally our dogs, use a predetermined ritual to express subjection. The point of such instincts is crystal clear: the preservation of the species has to be ensured. Tigers, lions, wolves and other powerfully armed species would risk extinction if their constant fighting inevitably led to the death of the defeated animal.

And what of man? In the age of chivalry the vanquished made a typical gesture of defeat. He removed his helmet and offered his unprotected head to the victor in sign of submission. We retain a memory of this gesture today when we take off our hats in greeting. But we do not really possess instincts of this vital nature in the true sense of the word, as the countless wars in our history have shown. In the age of the atomic bomb it can only be a question of our survival, of the vaunted human intelligence now persuading us to renounce genocidal wars against members of our own species.

But to get back to the instincts of animals. Modern research into behaviourism has brought so much new data to light that it would be beyond the framework of this book to describe it all in detail. We must perforce confine ourselves to certain important features, but the interested reader will find a wealth of detail in *Hunting without a Gun*, by Hermann Fischer and Dr. Heinz Woltereck (Heering-Verlag, Seebruck, 1960).

GOOD AND BAD MOTHERS IN THE ANIMAL WORLD

In no other realm of life does Nature show such a fantastic variety, such a wealth of methods of every conceivable kind as in the processes of procreation or, in other words, the preservation of the species. This applies equally to the task of fecundation as to the rearing of the young. Here Nature works alternately on an extensive or an intensive scale, with enormous numbers or with the most careful individual attention to the progeny. Fish, for example, fall into both categories. Most of them entrust their eggs to the water and there the matter ends as far as they are concerned. Astronomical figures are reached, and the female sometimes lays millions of eggs. The stickleback, on the contrary, lays a bare hundred or so, but in this instance the father, in the most touching manner, takes infinite trouble with his "children". First he builds a tube-shaped nest in which the female lays the eggs and which he fertilises immediately.

As soon as they are hatched he rigorously defends and cares for the young fry, and if they stray from the nest he catches them in his mouth and carries them back to safety. In the case of the sheat fish the male carries the eggs in his gullet, where the whole incubation takes place, and there they remain until they hatch. The male of another type carries the eggs in a special fold in the stomach, while yet another attaches them to his forehead with fibrous strands. The sea horse, to quote a further example of male rearing of the young, has a special pocket in which the female lays her eggs, where they develop during spawning time.

Sometimes the nursing on the part of the male is involuntary. The females of certain water bugs are in the habit of gluing their eggs on to the male's back. He does not seem at all happy about this because he usually tries to get rid of his burden. If successful, it is a poor look out for the progeny for he will probably devour them. On the other hand, the male of the midwife toad (*alytes obstetricans*) displays better paternal instincts. He winds the spawning cord round his hind legs and seeks some safe hiding place, and just before the young hatch he goes into the water so that the tadpoles will be in their right element.

Compared with the male, the activities of the female in the rearing of young are of infinite variety. The eggs are carried in every conceivable place—the legs, the belly or in some breeding pouch. The Surinam or honeycomb toad (*pipa americana*) derives her name from carrying her eggs in honeycomb-like depressions in the skin of her back. They hatch, go through the tadpole stage, and only leave their home when they are already small toads. Hence this responsible mother lays only a few dozen eggs, whereas most other toads lay considerably more, but the latter simply entrust them to the water.

In the insect world we find the most incredible instances of animal instinct regarding "child welfare". Most of the parents are long since dead when the young hatch, but they see to it, sometimes with the most subtle measures, that the latter will find favourable conditions for living. Butterflies and beetles know exactly what food the larvæ need and invariably lay their eggs on the "right" plants, even choosing special parts such as flower buds, young fruit, etc. The ichneumon wasp, with the aid of her ovipostor, lays her eggs in living creatures, above all caterpillars. She holds the record for ingenuity. Some of the ichneumonoidea can determine where and at what depth a woodworm is lodged in a completely healthy tree. With their long drill-like ovipostors they bore through the wood and stab the worm, which they do not see but only scent, with unfailing accuracy. Certain insects threatened by saw-flies and ichneumon wasps know how to protect their brood against predatory attacks. The mason bee, for example, lays her eggs in empty snail shells. After storing a sufficient supply of pollen and nectar in the snail shell, she lays her eggs and proceeds to make the larvæ's little house "ichneumon-proof". She closes the opening of the shell with a quick-congealing mortar and, as an additional safeguard against the long drill, will also build a roof of grass stalks, pine needles, etc. The ichneumon wasp builds little mud nests for its larvæ, leaving an insect inside for their future nourishment. To prevent the prey dying prematurely, it is not killed but merely paralysed by a sting. Many mutillid wasps leave a whole larder of insects, which will be eaten in succession by the larvæ.

True care of the young, where the parents participate in the hatching or birth as well as the rearing, we find in countless variations among birds and mammals. Some birds make the job easy for themselves by allowing the eggs to be hatched by the sun or, as in the case of the Australian megapode, by the heat generated in a cleverly stacked pile of leaves.

As everyone knows, the cuckoo leaves all the work to other birds, but this is an exception and most birds hatch their eggs by the warmth of their own bodies in more or less carefully constructed nests. Rearing reaches its peak in the mammals, which, in a graduated development, display ever better methods of caring for their issue. On the lowest rung of the ladder are the egg-laying mammals, such as the duck-billed platypus, fol-lowed by the marsupials, which carry their young in a pouch. As compared with the latter, whose young are born in a very undeveloped state, the offspring of most ungulates such as horses, chamois, etc., can follow their mother very soon after birth. The offspring of mammals, which come into the world completely helpless, have the advantage of a particularly lengthy after-care: they are protected against all dangers by their parents and occasionally given very far-reaching instruction for later life. Many people must have watched a pair of foxes teaching the cubs to stalk their prey, or a mother ape in the zoo bringing her young to order by thumps and smacks. Here the education of the younger generation has reached a particularly high level.

Incidentally, there is a clear connection between the degree of care in rearing and the number of offspring. The better the care of the young the smaller will be the number—from the millions of eggs in the case of fish, worms, etc., to the higher mammals which produce one young a year. This is by no means a disadvantage in the struggle for existence, as can be observed in the case of man. His rate of reproduction is certainly extraordinarily low compared with almost all other living creatures, but the physical and mental care of his young (we have only to think of the increasingly successful struggle against infant mortality) has been largely instrumental in achieving the rising population of the world.

CONDITIONS OF LIFE IN THE DEPTHS

As we know, life once originated in the sea, and only later was the dry land colonised. To a certain extent the animal cells took the sea with them on to the land in the form of their protoplasm, which, millions of years ago, created the prerequisite for the development of organisms on terra firma. Lower forms of marine life have, so to speak, salt water for blood. It flows through them, leaving a certain amount of oxygen behind and taking away the waste materials with it. At some point in the grey mists of time an organism closed its "open system" of arteries and veins and became an independent, gill-breathing creature. Such creatures were the ancestors of the first land animals. But even today salt water is used successfully as a temporary substitute for blood, and the acute observation of a biologist, who described the vascular system of the mammal as a "travelling bag of sea water", has some justification. A man weighing 135 lbs. consists of 95 lbs. water.

This gave rise to the idea that creatures from remote periods in the past could still exist today in the sea—the cradle of life— at least at great depths. Before the famous *Challenger* set sail in 1872 Darwin's most enthusiastic supporter, Thomas Huxley, spoke of the great hopes he entertained in this respect. "It is conceivable," he said, "that we shall bring to light zoological rareties which have remained unchanged in the depths of the ocean and have survived every catastrophe that proved so disastrous in shallow waters. They will give us some idea of the species that ruled the earth in the past."

Even today one often hears the opinion expressed that monsters which we have relegated to the realm of saga such as giant octopuses and, possibly, the notorious sea-serpent still lurk in the depths. The *Challenger* was four years at sea and with its deep-sea trawls brought up some very strange creatures from the sea bed. Among them were countless previously unknown fish with powerful jaws and remarkable luminous organs, strange creatures that only live "down below". But there were no sensations. All the catches could be incorporated in a fauna which was obviously related to the known animal world of the shallower depths and consisted only of special forms.

Nevertheless the voyage was of great significance for it heralded a new era in marine zoology. For the first time the *Challenger* had investigated the deeper parts of the seas round the world, as far as its equipment would allow. In the following decades a number of countries, including Germany, organised deep-sea expeditions with very limited objectives. Marine life gradually became known, more or less, down to a depth of 13,000 feet. But what were things like in the great depths? Until recently very little was known, although naturally it was a problem of vital interest. As we know, the greater part of our planet is covered with oceans. The actual deep sea—that part which reaches a depth of more than 13,000 feet—comprises about one third of the earth's surface. But until very recent times it represented an unexplored part of the globe. Of the animal life in the great depths, particularly the "trenches", which descend to more than 36,000 feet, we knew almost nothing until 1945. It seemed probable that these vast deeps could not afford any scope for life.

In the meantime that presumption has proved to be wrong. Life is "tough" enough to penetrate to the deepest parts of the ocean, and even to exist in the eternal ice of the polar regions, on high mountains and in barren steppe and desert.

In 1949 Russian deep-sea explorers brought up living organisms from a depth of over 26,000 feet, and they were followed by the extraordinarily successful expedition of the Danish ship *Galathea* (1950–52), which, with the aid of special equipment, investigated animal life at depths of more than 32,800 feet. The team used deep-sea trawls hung on 7½-mile hawsers and sea-bed shovels, apparatus which could be lowered to the bottom and pick up a certain amount of the "soil". In this way it could be determined how many organisms per square yard lived down below, and exact calculations could be made as to the density of life in the deepest parts of the ocean.

A few years ago many oceanographers of repute were of the opinion that there was no life below about 21,000 feet. This too was an error. The shovels and nets of the *Galathea* proved only too clearly that animal life exists at the greatest depths and, to our amazement, in great quantity and variety. The scientists of this research ship brought to the surface more than 100 different species from depths of between 19,500 and 32,500 feet. One single catch from just over 33,000 feet accounted for no less than 108 varieties.

The second possibility for exploring life below was direct observation with the aid of a new type of diving apparatus. In 1934 the American biologist William Beebe and his assistant were lowered in a sphere from a ship and succeeded for the first time in reaching a little over 3,000 feet, where they were able to watch the marine fauna through a quartz window. Since then this amazing achievement has been surpassed, thanks to revolutionary improvements in equipment. Before going to press the record stood at 35,800 feet, an incredible depth, which was reached by Jacques Piccard in the Marianas trench. As opposed to the sphere of Beebe and his successors, Piccard's new "bathyscaphe" has freedom of movement.

The third procedure involves the use of the underwater camera, a scientific tool of the greatest reliability which was recently lowered successfully to a depth of 32,500 feet. The camera is mounted on a stable carriage and descends from the ship in the same way as the sphere. When the framework touches sea bed the camera goes into action; it is then raised a little and lowered in a new position. With the aid of the electronic flash a series of more than a hundred shots can be taken on one of these dives. This new technique has proved that the greatest depths of the sea afford an asylum for life, although the upper regions are naturally more densely populated, because in them there is more to eat.

ANIMALS WITH "LAMPS"

Resourceful Nature has provided the inhabitants of the Stygian depths with a thoroughly adequate substitute for the lack of daylight. Since there is neither sun nor stars to provide light, they are able to illuminate themselves. On their descent, the bold divers witness a real firework display of magnificent light effects, the beauty and variety of which can only be appreciated by those who have been fortunate enough to see them. So far this experience has been reserved to very few. They reported that many fish are equipped with hundreds of lamps, while others suddenly turned on such powerful beams of light that the scientists in their dark sphere were almost blinded. From 19,500 feet down the inky depths are filled with the constant flickering and flashing of the luminous fish. During Beebe's dives the lights were so numerous that he was reminded of a starry sky on a clear night.

Many cuttlefish have quite spectacular luminous organs. One species sports a whole row of different coloured lamps, ranging from ultramarine to ruby red and sky blue. In many cases these various colours are produced direct: for example, the red light of this particular cuttlefish is caused by a red filter through which the light of the luminous organs has to pass. Another, a squid, which is only found at very great depths, carries huge white searchlights on its head and orange-coloured lamps at the tips of its long tentacles. Many deep sea animals, when pursued by their enemies, eject large quantities of a luminous substance in order to blind them.

Such light signals serve a host of purposes—scaring away enemies, enticing prey and, most important of all, the mutual recognition of the sexes. In the bright world above all manner of physical shapes, colours and smells are easy to recognise, but such distinguishing marks in the depths are replaced by predetermined light signals peculiar to each species. And we can see a feeble reflection of this welter of light on certain summer evenings when the fireflies are dancing. In their case, too, the little lamp is a message of love which brings the males and females together in the darkness.

This was proved by a very simple experiment. A female fire-fly which, as opposed to the male, keeps her light constantly burning, was imprisoned in a glass tube. The male fireflies, with their intermittent lights, were released above the illumin-ated container. Each time one of them flew over the female increased the power of her light, and this was immediately noticed by the males. Within a short space of time they col-lected in great numbers round the tube, and a real question-and-answer game between the sexes ensued by the increasing and dimming of the lights. To pursue the experiment the female was now enclosed in a porous cardboard box, which allowed scent or sound signals on the part of the female to pass through, but no light was visible. The sexes ignored each other, proving that the light alone brought them together.

The same attraction applies in the totally dark world of the deep-sea dwellers, except that their lights serve additional pur-poses. In order to attract their prey many of these monsters hang special lamps on long feelers in front of their jaws, others try to blind or terrify their opponents with lightning flashes. In the production of such luminous substances Nature once more surpasses any human technique: she works with chemical pro-cesses which take place in the luminous cells themselves, and the result is a perfectly cold light, an ideal which has so far not been achieved by our technicians. Electric bulbs transform a considerable part of the energy into unwanted heat: the animal lamps, on the contrary, record only the minutest increases in temperature on the most sensitive thermometer. Luminous bacteria play a great part in these living light effects. The Banda fish from East Indian waters, for instance, carries such bacteria permanently in a kind of gland in its body, and even cultivates them. Over the luminous organ lies a flap of skin, which enables the animal to extinguish its lamp. It seems that these very refined lighting devices are primarily designed for the recognition of the sexes, and the light signals are exchanged exactly as in the case of the fireflies.

LIFE IN THE OCEAN DEPTHS

There is no better example of life's extraordinary adaptability to its environment than that displayed by the bizarre creatures living in the ocean depths. They are quite impervious to the fantastically high water pressure, which would crush a man out-side the diving sphere or bathyscaphe to pulp in a fraction of a second. But the deep-sea dwellers have no gas compartments in their bodies—their tissue is filled with fluid—and because, as we know, it is difficult to compress water their organisms are not affected by the colossal external pressure.

What is the situation regarding food? As in the case of all other animals, deep-sea fish depend upon the presence of the first link in the nutrition chain—green plants. Only they are capable, with the aid of solar energy, of forming those food-stuffs which render possible the existence of animals (and humans). In the ocean the primary source of food is vegetable plankton. This is composed of small plants, visible only under the microscope, which appear in vast masses, serving, in the first instance, as food for the minute animal plankton and, subsequently, as food for the larger marine fauna, making possible their existence both directly and indirectly. To carry out the building of energy-rich foodstuffs the vegetable plankton naturally needs sunlight. Now this condition only exists in the upper water levels. The rays of the sun do not penetrate much more than 300 feet, and so the productivity of these upper levels is of capital importance. The output varies from sea to sea, but as a whole is surprisingly high. It has recently been claimed that the foodstuff production of the sea corresponds in bulk to the harvest of all the land surfaces of the earth.

All life in the depths is therefore dependent upon the harvest of the so-called productive levels, in other words upon the food that sinks slowly down from above. In these circumstances it is surprising how prolific life still is on the ocean bed. According to the latest findings it amounts to approximately 1 gramme per square yard. "Dead zones", or regions where there is no life, seem to be non-existent.

One of the relevant problems has now been solved by the work of German zoologists—viz. the question of the vitamin supply of deep sea animals. Samples of the Atlantic bed, raised by the Fisheries Research ship *Anton Dohrn*, were preserved and later examined in the Institute for Marine Research (Bremer-haven). It was found that these samples contained tiny living creatures of the yeast fungus type, which feed down below on dissolved material and produce important vitamins. Moreover they destroy organic remains that sink to the bottom and give them vitamin value. When a higher marine animal consumes these fungi, which are found in great masses, it not only absorbs nutritious substances but vitamins—at a depth of 16,000 to 26,000 feet below the surface!

GIANT SHARKS AND "ELECTRIC" FISH

The oft-reported sea serpent, though it has never actually been proved to exist, is in all probability a fish. The first candidate to come under review is the blue shark, a powerful but very peaceful denizen of the sea, which reaches a length of more than 26 feet and delights in swimming with other members in single file close to the surface, when it can easily be mistaken for a "sea serpent". But there are other fish that produce the same effect from a distance, notably an inhabitant of the great depths which very seldom surfaces and is therefore rarely seen. On these occasions the observer is faced with a very strange sight—a rather small animal of average length with a muzzle like a horse, pitch black jaws, strange "feelers" on the head and a bluish zebra-striped belly. On account of its bodily shape this curious beast is known as a "strapfish". It is completely harmless and is certainly not a sea serpent.

The largest of all known fish is the whale shark, which lives in tropical waters and can reach a length of 65 feet. It has mighty jaws, within which, when fully extended, a medium-sized man could stand upright. This giant fish is also completely harmless. It lives, like the blue shark, off small marine life, and there is no recorded case of one of these plankton-eaters ever attacking a man.

Far smaller but decidedly more sinister are those fish that can give electric shocks. This character in animals is undoubtedly very remarkable, and it has only developed in the fish phylum, moreover in an extraordinarily practical and effective form. Each muscle when in play produces an "action current". In the course of millions of years Nature has enabled the species to develop electric organs which work on the principle of a galvanic element. The most effective form of such an organ is to be found in the electric eel, which is widely distributed in South America and lives mainly in tropical waters, muddy brooks and marshes. These creatures can be 6 feet in length, and their electric organs lie on either side of the spinal column and extend along four fifths of their length.

They are nothing less than electric batteries with cells of a glutinous substance—former muscle tissue transformed into thousands of small columnar plates set in successive rows. Each of these represents an electric cell, and the capacity of all the cells aggregate on the principle of an ordinary multi-celled battery. Measurements have shown that a powerful electric eel can give a shock corresponding to 300 to 400 volts. The electric capacity of these living batteries has been determined as developing up to 1,600 watts.

No wonder, then, that a shock from one of these eels can be very painful to a man and can render him unconscious, and he may drown. When hunting the creature swims close to its prey —fish, crabs, etc.—numbing them in a split second with the aid of its battery. Observations have shown that young crocodiles have no chance against an electric eel; the voracious saurian is numbed before it can become really dangerous.

The electric ray or torpedo fish lives mainly in the warm seas and an encounter with one, for example while bathing in the Mediterranean, is far from pleasant. As in the case of the eel its electric organ developed down the ages from original muscle tissue. Its effect is not so powerful as that of the eel, but it is enough to numb smaller animals and to give a man a very nasty shock.

In African waters we find the electric catfish, a creature of about 3 feet in length, capable of giving shocks up to 200 volts. This fish only hunts at night, but it has unusually weak eyes and cannot see in the dark water. It was formerly thought that it "sought out" its prey with the aid of the feelers on its head, but this would be impossible at any distance. How, then, does the electric catfish hunt? The problem was recently solved by a British biologist, Dr. Lissman (Cambridge), with very intriguing results. The investigations he carried out off the African coast showed that the fish can use its electric organ as a kind of radar apparatus. It sends out a series of impulses, creating an electric field, which will be disturbed by any obstacles in its vicinity such as stones, fish, etc. With the aid of a receiving organ it picks up these disturbances and is able to find its bearings. So it can not only give shocks but also "locate" electrically, because, as opposed to the electric eel, its electric organ consists not of former muscle tissue but of epithelial cells transformed for the purpose.

The skin is known to fulfil a host of sensory functions, reacting to the touch and to differences of temperature, etc. The skin of this African electric fish has apparently taken over the function of a "position-finding" apparatus. It appears that it generates two types of electric charge, one direct and the other alternating. The former must serve for orientation and the latter for paralysing the prey. The creature receives its information via the "receptor organs" in the skin and can then avoid obstacles even in complete darkness. A parallel case is to be found in the bat. The latter uses short waves, while the electric fish works with a radar apparatus. The marvels of Nature never fail to astound.

THE STRANGEST OF ALL: RADIOACTIVE FISH

An American deep sea expedition in the area of the Philippines recently brought up from a depth of 16,000 feet the most remarkable fish that has yet been observed. It was a so-called "hooked" ray, weighing 14 cwt., and possessing no less than 36 luminous organs, whose electric capacity equalled 1,800 watts. But that was not all, for this native of the deep was also radioactive. In addition to visible light it transmitted penetrating rays stronger than the combined radiation of 10 X-ray tubes. Naturally the fishing continued, and a few days later a searchlight fish, with a radioactivity three times greater than had been measured in the hooked ray was caught. It turned out that in this species the radiation is transmitted from luminous organs located beneath the eyes. The questions now arose: what was the origin of the materials that made the radiation possible, and what purpose could such a coupling of visible light and penetrating radiation serve in the searchlights of this fish?

The first question can be answered with certainty, and the second only by conjecture. The deepest parts of the ocean, the so-called trenches, extend in part over strata of the sea bed containing a comparatively high content of radioactive minerals. The water constantly dissolves some of them, and small amounts of such substances are absorbed in the tissue of the fish in question. The second problem is more complicated. It would appear that Nature gave special aids to deep-sea inhabitants in their particularly difficult struggle for existence. Their multifarious and effective luminous organs are a clear example of this.

It is logical to suppose that the radio-activity of the sea bed and of the deep water is exploited to a certain extent by the creatures living down there. An "improvement" of the luminous organs became possible, until they could transmit visible, invisible and even ionising rays, which had a corresponding effect on the receptor organs. There is no scientific confirmation of this, but it seems probable for it lies, so to speak, in line with Nature's procedure. By an incredible variety of methods she sees to it that even her least successful creations have a guaranteed existence. Hence the exploitation of radioactive sea bed substances can be of additional advantage to the "information service" of the animals in question.

On the other hand, how is it that they obviously suffer no harm from radiation, which in normal conditions—i.e. in all forms of life on the earth's surface or in the upper levels of the sea—would undoubtedly have a most deleterious effect? Presumably we must regard this in the light of adaptability resulting from selection through suitable mutations. In the course of time particularly radiation-resistant individuals chanced to survive and procreate. Time and time again Nature shows that she is capable of giving a "chance" to her creations even under the most unfavourable conditions, and this applies equally to organisms which have to live under extreme pressure, extreme radiation, in complete darkness, and under the most difficult conditions for finding food. The fulfilment of all these conditions seems incredible to man's "logical" mind, but the inhabitants of the deep exist all the same.

ANIMALS AND PLANTS IN THE EARTH'S ECONOMY

There are about 350,000 known species of plants, as opposed to more than a million species of animals. These figures are by no means complete for each year new types of animal are discovered, but the catalogue to date shows that the diversity of animals is far greater than that of plants. How did this come about? For years changing environmental conditions, with their manifold selective influences, led to ever new gene combinations which gave living creatures a chance of stabilisation on the path of selection. The brighter the mosaic pattern of environmental factors, the greater the variety of life. But the environment of plants is comparatively uniform, for in the last analysis climate and soil are the determining factors. Other species-forming factors play a very minor role, whereas they can be of the utmost importance to the animal. The very fact that many animals live on plants enormously increases the effect of external conditions and, in the course of long geological periods, affords countless possibilities for minor or major changes.

Recent research has shown surprisingly great differences in the ecological distribution of the two great groups of living organisms. A rough estimate of the total mass of plants existing on the earth today shows that they would fill a space of about 2,300 cubic kilometres. On the other hand, all the animals and men together would fill only a space of barely 2 cubic kilometres. The proportion 2 : 2,300 (animals : plants) is naturally purely arbitrary, for in the case of most animals we can only strike an approximate figure for the individuals. Man alone is the exception. His total of 2,600 million individuals would occupy a space of about 130 million cubic metres (metres not kilometres!) We can afford to be "bold" in our estimates, for even if the volume of 2 cubic kilometres (animals and men) errs in either direction, it would not alter the fact that the human and animal content of the dry land is insignificant compared with that of plants.

Very different is the relevant comparison between the animal and the plant masses in the original home of all living creatures, the water. American biologists have recently made extensive surveys in several oceans of the proportions of animal and plant substance, and have arrived at figures ranging between 1 : 7 and 1 : 20. If in all the oceans we take into account the plankton community alone, in other words free-moving organisms in water, we obtain an average proportion of 1 : 14 (animals : plants). In the seas, as compared with the land, the relative proportion of animal substance is also far higher.

The reason for these interesting facts is not too difficult to find. The sea in general is far better colonised than the land by the lower and usually smaller forms of life—plankton consist almost exclusively of microscopic living creatures. (As regards volume, fish account for only 2% of the living substance in the water.) The smaller the organism, the earlier it matures and is capable of fecundation, and the faster reproduction ensues. This is why the numerical relationship between animals and plants in the water is considerably higher than on land.

We have already described how, in the remote past, plants made the great leap out of the water on to dry land so that it could also become a living space for animals. However, to adapt themselves to the new conditions, the animals had to overcome far greater difficulties than the more simply constructed plants because their inner organisation is more complicated and, in consequence, more demanding.

The animal kingdom, down the ages, split into an unending variety of species, whereas the plants did not need to do so on such a scale—an important basis for the fact that the number of plants so greatly exceeds that of animals. In compensation the plants predominate all the more in volume, because only a small fraction of the organic masses they produce is used by the land animals. In the water a different value prevails. Here the vegetable substance is used by the animals a hundred times more efficiently than on land.

THE SIGNIFICANCE OF PLANT CULTIVATION

Our "world history" would have been impossible had man not discovered farming. At the outset only seeds and fruit of the wild plants were gathered, but in the long run they proved inadequate. As early as the Stone Age the cultivation of useful plants began, and after thousands of working years the wild plants were finally transformed into cultivated varieties. Very early in time the cereals—millet, wheat and barley—were developed from grasses. The pile builders already knew flax and certain leguminous plants, which, during the Bronze Age, were complemented by rye, oats, beets and a few types of fruit. This development continued for thousands of years. New plants were added and finally, in modern times, came the discovery of heredity, whose laws gave us new possibilities of outwitting Nature with her own weapons and creating plants which had never before existed.

Modern scientific agriculture can improve the plants in question, and today more can be achieved in a decade than was possible during many centuries of observation and experience. We have by no means come to the end of the road—in fact, we may even be only at the beginning. The human race increases rapidly and its demands for food increase proportionately. Useful plants with a bigger yield, cereals that ripen earlier, etc., are imperative. The most effective methods seem to be the selection of individual plants for cultivation and cross-breeding whereby use is made, according to need, of cultivated forms alone or additional wild plants. Let us imagine that two plants differ only in 10 hereditary characters. When they are crossed more than 1,000 different combinations result! The cultivator need only choose the most suitable forms for his purpose—man has done this for centuries—and can in this way continue to extend the vegetable basis of our food.

The Stone Age peasant had a far easier task than that which faces us today. He merely used the best plants for further cultivation, and they sufficed for his primitive needs. Today we are more demanding. For instance, Baur, the wizard of Müncheberg, had to test a million and a half lupins in order to find five specimens of the "sweet variety"—i.e. plants devoid of bitter material. In this arduous way he succeeded in producing his famous sweet lupins, which can be eaten by cattle and represent a very valuable protein-rich fodder.

THE SUCCESSES OF THE PLANT HUNTERS

In Canada's wheat country grain has been cultivated systematically by continued crossing to fulfil the demands of the prevailing climate. This is the origin of the wheat known as "maquis", which ripens ten days before the normal kind. The comparatively small difference in time means a gain of about 100 million dollars a year for Canadian farmers, simply because this wheat will ripen even in the north of the country during Canada's shorter harvesting period. Besides countless crossings of cultivated species we turn more and more today to the original wild plants, which have not been so tampered with as our long suffering "useful" plants. A particularly dry summer or an unfavourable winter can wreak havoc in our fields, but wild plants, in their natural struggle for existence, have become in-

ured to difficult living conditions. Modern agriculture, therefore, is inclined to exploit more efficiently than before the inexhaustible reserve of wild plants.

At present only about 2,000 out of 350,000 known species of
plant are used agriculturally, and many more could certainly
be brought into the service of mankind. We are making every
effort to combine the productive wealth of our cultivated plants
with the toughness to climate, resistance to disease and other
good characters of wild plants, and we have already met with
considerable success. Today the whole earth is being systematically combed to find new species that can be used to advantage.
To specialists in the field, passionate plant hunters by profession, modern man with his great need for food owes more
than is generally realised.

Let us take a few examples of this work from the many that
spring to mind. The German Hindukush expedition brought
back from Afghanistan a particularly hardy wheat selected
from hundreds of test seeds. The Hindukush wheat was crossed
with Argentinian wheat and a variety was produced which is
so insensitive to frost that it can even be harvested under the
snow. By crossing the European potato with the wild potato
from Guatemala German farmers produced a tuber which is
almost impervious to cold and the much dreaded leaf mould.

The American Minister for Agriculture organised a thirty-
year search for a date palm suitable for growing in Arizona and
California. Year after year the plant hunters combed the
oases of Algiera and Tunisia, the date plantations of Baghdad
and the Middle East—and after endless trouble the right date
palm was found. It is now being grown in the States with great
success. American plant hunters and cultivators have aided
agriculture with winter-hardy almond trees, wheat that is resistant to drought, and many new types of useful plant from
which food for millions of people is grown.

Russia, later the Soviet Union, has always had outstanding
agriculturists whose work is of vital importance to that country,
because it has vast areas in which, for climatic reasons, normal
useful plants do not thrive. One of the most celebrated was Ivan
Mitschurin, to whom both his country and the world should
be deeply grateful. Originally a precision tool-maker, he went
to live in the remote town of Koslov—today known as

Mitschurinsk—as an "unobtrusive recluse in an experimental nursery", as he puts it. During the First World War he grew cold-resistant corn and fruit in a small experimental garden. Lenin heard of him and gave him his support, with the result that the Koslov garden became a point of departure for a very significant development in agriculture and fruit growing. Mitschurin's work enabled the Soviet Union to push its fruit-growing frontier far to the north. He developed in all more than 300 new types of plants, including frost-hardy bushes and new types of fruit by crossing bullaces and plums.

Of special importance, too, was a completely new cultivated species which Mitschurin arrived at by crossing a wild plant from the forests of Eastern Manchuria with other plants, pro-ducing a kind of grapevine substitute for the north of the Soviet Union. A no less audacious step was taken by another Soviet specialist, N. Zizin, who crossed wheat with one of the worst weeds of the fields and the bane of every peasant—couch grass. This "street urchin" of the plant world is unbelievably tough and can survive in the most unfavourable surroundings. After year-long experiments, by crossing cultivated wheat with a certain sub-species of couch grass, Zizin succeeded in growing a particularly resistant type of wheat which has proved its stabil-ity under the most testing conditions.

In modern horticulture mutations naturally play a very prominent part, for Nature offers, so to speak, ample material for experimentation. An attempt was recently made to induce suitable mutations for plant cultivation artificially, e.g. by radiation. We have already mentioned that such possibilities exist, but would they achieve anything of value to agriculture? Scientists were sceptical to begin with, for most of the artificially produced mutations only resulted in a degeneration of the prototype. Recently, however, a Swedish cultivator, Gus-tavsson, achieved results which promise great things for the future. He subjected thriving barley to X-rays, and later sowed the seeds. He was able to observe literally hundreds of mutations, most of which were valueless, but, finally, among the 700 mutants he found one which led to an improvement upon the original plant. Gustavsson had aimed at a new strain of barley which would yield a richer harvest than any type pre-viously grown in Sweden and would have stronger stalks and earlier ripening grain. The cultivation of this plant proved interesting. In Southern Sweden it yielded a poorer harvest than the mother plant, but in the raw climate of the north the harvest increased by more than a quarter. The experience proves that wild species exist which under normal conditions are ill-suited to agriculture but which will thrive in a cold climate.

ANIMALS THAT HELP US

Basically the same processes used in plant cultivation are exploited by man in the breeding of his domestic animals. His first animal helper was the dog, which Palæolithic man already accepted into his family circle. We know, from Mesolithic finds some 12,000 years old, of the existence of two breeds of house dogs differing clearly from their wild ancestors. The dog must therefore have been a helper of man at an earlier date. Perhaps wolf cubs were tamed, just as we occasionally bring a young deer or a baby stork into the house. Further, we know that in the Neolithic domestic animals such as dogs, cattle, pigs and sheep were kept in great numbers. We do not know a great deal about the circumstances of the change-over from wild to domestic animals. Sometimes it may have been comparatively simple, as in the case of captured wolf cubs, from which, in the course of time, our dogs have developed. Presumably Stone Age hunters sometimes brought home the young of a wild sow they had killed, and in this way obtained the original material for breeding the domestic pig. In any case, the domestication of animals, as with plant cultivation, led to the creation of many strains. We know, for example, more than 500 varieties of our domestic pigeon, whereas its ancestor, the wild ring dove, has remained a single species. A comfortable existence under the protection of man has not always improved the character of the animal. We need only compare the cunning and foolhardy courage of the wild sheep with the docile patience of our gentle purveyor of wool.

But man cannot afford to heed such sentimental view-points. He breeds his domestic animals for his own purpose—the cow for its milk yield, the pig for bacon, meat, etc. The results of his farming activities are too well known for comment, and we shall confine ourselves to a few words on the scientific bases of animal breeding. Darwin already recognised that the races of our domestic animals stem from a thousand years of artificial breeding—such facts inspired him to outline his theory of natural selection. In the field of cultivated plants man allows the characters of certain species to develop, then, by further crossing, tries to enhance or suppress any characters that may suit his purpose. The astounding variety of our present-day domestic animals came about in this way. Moreover they have managed, under the unnatural conditions of human protection, to survive mutations which, in the wild state, would have caused them to be rejected as unfit for survival. It is very difficult to imagine that a dog with the bandy legs of a dachshund could exist for very long in the wild. Man, however, continued to breed this little "natural joke", with the result that our blithe race of dachshunds continues to thrive. Hornless cattle, pigeons with huge tails, snow-white rabbits, pigs so fat that they can hardly move, and other artificial products of our breeders would be highly unsuited to life in the wild. Incidentally, many domestic animals are subject to frequent mutations, and in this way a variety of specialised strains can be bred. Rabbit breeders among our readers will be interested to note that their favourite pet is particularly prone to mutations, and that is why it is so easy to "change".

LIVING CREATURES WE DO NOT KNOW

The multiplicity of life on earth makes it comprehensible that a long time passed before zoologists were able to obtain a fair overall picture, at least of the larger animals. It was not until recent times that man really conquered the earth and that most of the remaining blank patches on the map could be filled in. The inaccessible polar regions and the huge primeval forests of the tropics have been surveyed in part by aircraft, and therefore only superficially in the true sense of the word. In 1926 a long mountain chain 1,000 miles in length, with several 10,000-feet peaks, could still be "discovered" in Eastern Siberia in a region which was marked on the map as "undulating lowland". If such little surprises can still lie in store for the modern geographer, the geologist must be on the alert.

As we have already stated, no further surprises are to be expected in the future with regard to land vertebrates, but on the other hand there are thousands of insects we do not know. The greater possibilities for new discoveries are undoubtedly in the ocean depths. Science has only comparatively recently started exploring the oceans, and this vast living space still contains many animals that no human eye has seen. Are there new "monster" forms down there? Enthusiastic specialists in deep-sea fishing have discovered swordfish and sharks of hitherto unsuspected dimensions. Occasionally some "sea monster" may be spotted or washed ashore to arouse bitter controversy among the experts. Severed tentacles point to the existence of gigantic octopuses (*cephalopoda*) which no one has ever seen, and a strange marine animal stranded a few years ago at Cape Hay still remains unclassified.

Meanwhile our professional era has discredited the numerous fabulous beasts with which men of olden times in their imagination peopled the earth. This applies to the sea serpent as much as to the century-old belief in the unicorn. The latter never existed in the alleged form, and it was possibly an exaggerated description of the rhinoceros. The giant vampires and the man-eating dragons also belong to the realm of fable, but in both cases it is comparatively easy to see how such beliefs arose. As we know, there are certain types of bat living today in tropical regions which drink the blood of animals, and it is perhaps possible that they could tap off blood from a sleeping man. In South America there is one species known as the Great Vampire bat. These creatures certainly live up to their name but would hardly cause serious damage, at any rate to humans, except that they are known disease-carriers.

And what of the dragon? It undoubtedly existed in the time of the dinosaurs, but those giants of the animal kingdom were extinct long before the first primitive forms of man existed. Nevertheless modern zoology knows certain monitors which might easily be termed dragons—one is actually called the Komodo dragon—but they are far too small to spell any danger to man.

We must mention here another mysterious creature that is talked about from time to time—the Tatzelwurm. It has long played a certain part in Alpine folk lore. According to report, it hisses and spits at men on sight. The Tatzelwurm certainly never existed, and the eye-witness accounts must have

been exaggerated descriptions of adders on the move or schel-
topusiks (glass snakes). This member of the lizard family
occasionally wanders from its native Balkans into the Alps, but
it is neither mysterious nor dangerous.

Science anticipates, on the other hand, serious new discoveries in remote unexplored regions such as small islands, cave
areas, etc. Special forms, of which we certainly know nothing,
could have developed in such conditions. We have only to
think of the cave crayfish and the cave proteus from the giant
Kentucky caves, and of those interesting dwarf forms from
remote regions such as dwarf zebus, Shetland ponies and dwarf
hippopotami.

IS THE FORMATION OF NEW SPECIES AT AN END?

There are certain indications that, at least in the main line
of evolution, the building of new species is at an end. Since the
last Ice Age, and probably since the appearance of the first
man, no really new group of living creatures has arisen. Viewed
within the vast span of geological time, there is naturally no
proof that this situation will continue, but for the moment we
can observe only comparatively minor changes in our present-
day stock of terrestrial fauna. Incidentally, the concept
"species" is fairly elastic, for basically it is merely an arbitrary
division within the broad framework of systematics. The
myriads of living forms in Nature cannot be fitted so easily into
a rigid scheme, and thus the usual definition of a species is
constantly being upset by exceptions. A species implies that a
population of individuals should reproduce naturally, perpetu-
ating their own "species".

Horse and donkey belong to two different species, but their
hybrid, the mule, is nearly always sterile. On the other hand,
there are many undoubtedly genuine species which, despite our
fine definition, produce fertile progeny when crossed. An
accurate demarcation of forms is therefore hardly possible. To
facilitate matters we split the species into various sub-species
(local forms, clines, etc.), renouncing any attempt to apply the
clear-cut concept of species in every case. However, the biologist has to cling to this term for he urgently needs taxonomy to
preserve some order in his catalogue of living creatures.

Even if the creation of major types of living creature appears to be at an end, individual differentiation continues, and it is certain that here and there the formation of a new species occasionally occurs. In the plant kingdom there are special cases where, by crossing two species, a new one is bred. Such an event was observed some years ago in the evening primrose (*œnothera*), which thrives on our refuge dumps. The hybrids of two species developed into a new species whose individuals were capable of reproduction, but they no longer followed the Mendelian law of segregation and they remained sterile with regard to the parent plants. Such cases of new species-formation are quite common among plants. A weed of our cornfields, the red hemp nettle (*galeopsis tetrahit*), also developed from two different species. Since the two points of departure for this new strain were known, a very interesting experiment was made to try and reconstruct the event. Thousands of crossings were carried out and the experiment finally succeeded. From one of these crossings a red hemp nettle was bred in the precise form we have long since known in Nature. Here the geneticist used the chemist's technique of artificial syntheses to produce a new species in the laboratory, so to speak.

In another instance we can even determine the actual date when a new speciation took place. In England in 1870 rice-grass (*Spartina townsendii*) was discovered and recognised at once as a completely new species. Within the next few years the new plant spread over large coastal areas of England and France. It was then conveyed to the German North Sea coast, as it promised to be a great aid in the reclaiming of land. The sowing turned out, if anything, to be too effective, for the rice-grass overgrew other plants which had already been used successfully for the binding of newly won soil. How did this costly plant originate? One of its primitive forms is *Spartina stricta*, a grass that has been known for 300 years in Europe; the other, *Spartina alternifolia*, was imported into England from America in 1840. So the speciation must have occurred in the thirty years between 1840 and 1870.

These examples must suffice. They show clearly enough the modest framework in which the remodelling of living forms takes place in the present geological period of the earth's history. Each new breed of domestic animal, each further success of the modern wizards of horticulture, is basically a new creation of a living form. But it all takes place, we might say, on the fringe of evolution. The changes are nuances, small and significant, within the overall and highly variegated pattern of life on earth which was laid down in the far distant past. It is possible that on our planet none of the former frequent revolutions in the building of its inhabitants will occur again, but it could be that in the distant future new dynasties of living creatures will replace the present ones. We do not know, and we will have to leave this problem to our descendants of the next hundred thousand years.

CHAPTER VI

The Functions of Life

THE organism of man, and incidentally of higher life, has been compared with a well-run state in which each section has a specific task to fulfil, so that all can co-operate ideally for the common good. Today we speak of the "cell state" and know that this comparison is appropriate. We have seen that the cells, of which the bodies of multicellular living creatures are formed, represent tiny building-blocks of unlimited variety. In certain circumstances they enjoy a high degree of independence, although they invariably work in the interest of the whole, whereby certain cells amalgamate into tissue and the latter into an organ, which, for its part, is indispensable to the functioning of the whole "cell state". These organs also work in close co-operation, mutually exerting such a strong influence that, on the collapse of a single organ, the further existence of the entire organism is gravely imperilled. In a confusing wealth of the most varied processes Nature sees to it that, with the aid of the nervous system, the blood circulation, hormones, etc., the complicated structure of the body, despite constant renewal of individual parts, functions as a harmonious whole. If we wish to understand the functions of life we must take a closer look at the working methods of the organs and the various organic systems.

NATURE AS ENGINEER

A great bridge over the river has been blown up in war and has to be rebuilt. In the planning office the chief designer stands by his drawing-board and checks the blueprints. A beautifully swung trellis of steel is to span the river. The load capacity and solidity of the girders and bracings are calculated. What the architects build here out of steel Nature builds on amazingly similar lines, on the girder system, in the bodies of all higher life—the bones. Each of these represents an intricately built part suited to its particular task down to the last detail. Moreover it fulfils this task with the least use of material, achieving the maximum solidity. How comparatively recent is the discovery that, mass for mass, solid iron poles are not necessarily the firmest, and how old is Nature's trick of using hollow bones to support limbs? The burdens they have to support differ in weight, and they are strongest at the extremities. By dissecting a bone we can see the wonderful girderwork in which the trabeculæ are so arranged that they follow the lines of thrust and traction. This is the same principle as is used in modern bridge construction. Even the curves of the bracings are the same. At school or in some museum we may have seen the "scaffolding" of the body, the skeleton, and we know that it represents a construction at once rigid and mobile. The combination of these two qualities is of the greatest importance. Let us imagine our plight if, let us say, Nature, on the principle of our bridge-builders, had given us a rigid skeleton to carry about. . . . Fortunately Nature obtains the necessary solidity with very light materials—calcium deposited in osseous tissue—plus an arrangement of "buffers", such as the thick discs of cartilage between the vertebræ, so that the joints of the scaffolding remain elastic.

On the formation of bone from the basic calcic substance and the so-called bone cells, the whole structure is, as it were, put together "in rough". Hardly is this complete, than other cells, the "perforators", come into action and bore a hole lengthwise through the bone. They hollow it in a certain prescribed manner, giving it its final form. The nerve cells move into the cavity, and from these the marrow is formed. By a combination of connective tissue and calcium in the bone formation, they become both hard and elastic. Despite all economical measures the weight of the scaffolding is still great enough to set clear limitations on the growth of the organism. As the body weight increases, the relative weight of the skeleton follows suit. In the shrewmouse, for example, it represents only 8% of the total body weight, and in humans about 18%. This also explains the fact that the real giants of the animal world are only to be found in the water! Its buoyancy relieves them of a great part of the body's weight. Thus the size of a whale can be fifty times that of an elephant, and those extinct giants, the saurians, usually inhabited swamps and streams. The skeletal construction in all vertebrates is on the same principle, although the special tasks of the individual bones have led to the development of different forms.

Ingenious Nature has not confined herself to the formation of the internal skeleton of vertebrates, but has devised completely different methods of solving the same problem—light scaffolding with the greatest mobility—in insects, spiders and other arthropods. They have a carapace of chitin, which is as strong as it is light. The necessary elasticity is provided by the interposition of movable areas. Other animals build exoskeletons from calcium or silicic acid. In the course of centuries huge deposits of chalk have piled up—we can see them today in our mountains as a sign that at one time they were below the sea —from the tiny calcic armour of the single-celled marine foraminiferæ which proliferated in the water. Architects of the same stature are the corals, which continue to build islands and reefs as in the past.

THE BUILDING ART OF PLANTS

We find similar achievements in the plant world. The diatoms, for example, build their protective armour in such a variety of forms that, from the shape and construction of the "shells", several thousand species of these diminutive architects can be distinguished. But by and large every cornstalk is an astounding natural masterpiece from which the engineer can learn a great deal but which he cannot copy. We must consider that a cornstalk is built in the proportion of 1 : 500 with regard to diameter and height, and that the tall structure on its minute base can carry heavy ears whose weight is many times that of the stalk.

Moreover the weight is not merely borne but the stalk sways to and fro in the wind, allowing itself to be forced down to the ground, only to right itself again. Such effects are achieved by a wonderful combination of different "technical devices". For a start, the osmotic pressure of the cytoplasm on the cell walls sees to it that the supporting "skin" of the stalk remains constantly taut, and that the whole plant body preserves its tension and elasticity. This buttressing is completely adequate in smaller plants that grow near the ground, but corn and other plants with lofty stems are aided by long, tough bast fibres for the additional strengthening of the "building". Exactly as in the case of bones, the maximum solidity is achieved with a minimum use of material. This occurs according to the most modern technological principles—the arrangement of the "scaffolding" tissue in tubular form, as we find in tubular steel girders, the use of stiffeners on the lines of T-girders, the spiral course of the fibres in order to achieve strength of torsion, etc. The nodes of the stalk are a masterpiece. They serve not only for strengthening but see to it that the stalk can raise itself again, for if it has sunk after heavy rain, the cells of the nodes on the underside grow stronger than those on the upper; the node also bends like a knee joint, lifting the stalk in this way back to its vertical position.

When the demands on the plant skeleton increase, more substantial means have to be employed—supports of solid material. This we find in the wood of trees which, thanks to its solidity, can reach very considerable heights. The wood pulp, or lignite, is also stored in tubular form in the cells. Incidentally, we can read from the rings in the trees how the girth increased at different speeds according to the season and climatic conditions. Despite this extraordinarily efficient supporting framework even trees cannot rise "to the sky". Size and weight with increasing height, and the ever-expanding treetop and the necessary resistance to wind, pose insuperable limitations even in the case of the giant trees of California and Africa.

THE MYSTERIOUS MUSCLES

Fortunately we can use our musculature without having to know its formation and activity in detail. Each hand movement would be very clumsy if we had to think each time which of the countless muscles in the hand had to be brought into play. Nature spares us a great many such reflections because the so-called smooth or non-striated muscular tissue functions involuntarily. These involuntary muscles are arranged longitudinally in two main layers; they include most of the muscles of the bowel. The voluntary or striated muscles, on the contary, have the capacity to contract on the orders of the nerves that control them. All swiftly reacting muscles fall into this category. The heart is an exception, being formed of a network of transverse striated muscles.

Phosphorescent fish which William Beebe observed from his bathy-scaphe for the first time at a depth of 2,600 ft. The steel diving globe is lowered from the parent ship by cable.

The long-leafed sundew has pointed digestive glands on its leaves.
They exude a sticky fluid to trap small insects which are subsequently
digested.

The seeds of many plants, like the thistle seed shown here, have floating apparatus which enables them to cover great distances.

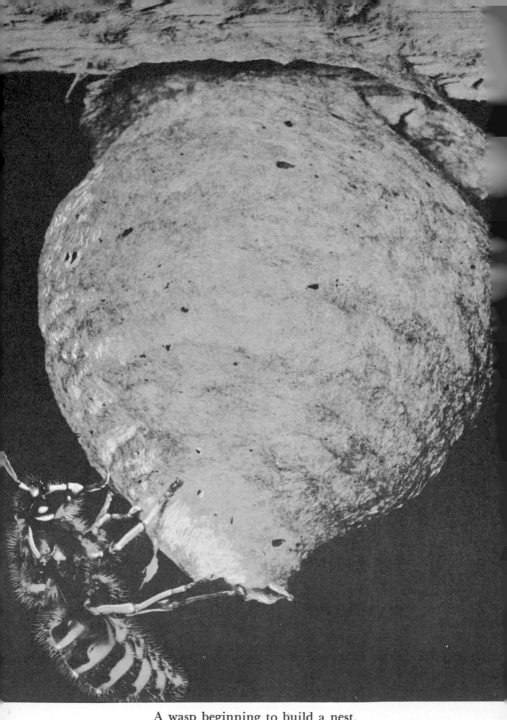

A wasp beginning to build a nest.

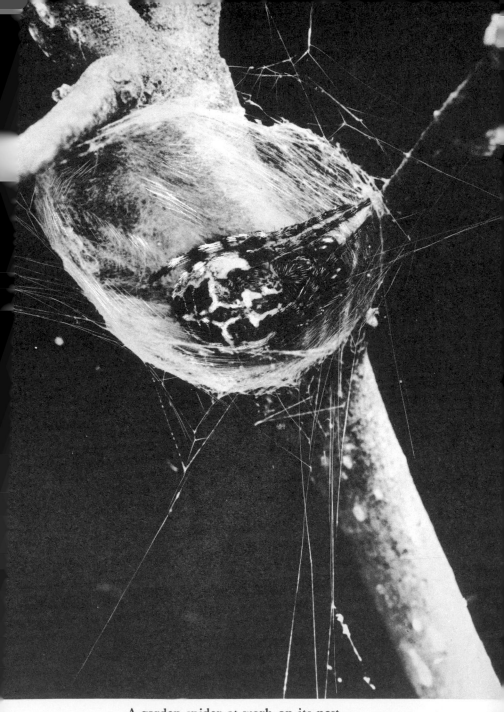

A garden spider at work on its nest.

The expressive face of a grasshopper.

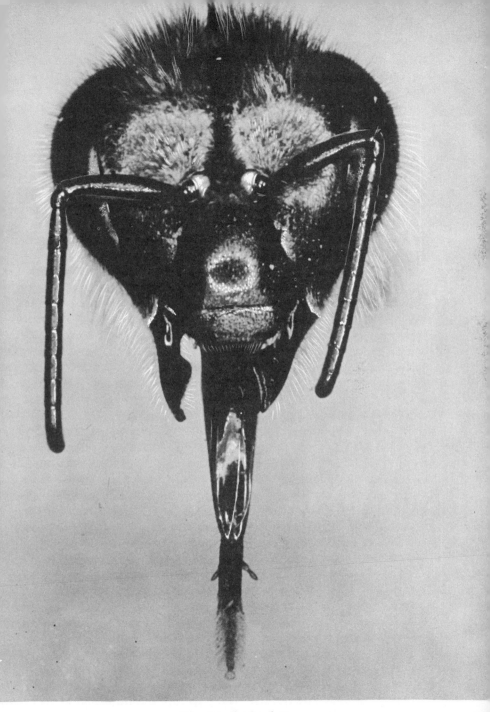

The head of a bee.

The ant is in the attacking posture, ready to squirt formic acid at its enemy.

The working methods of a muscle are extraordinarily complicated. Its activity can be looked upon as that of a chemico-dynamic machine; in fact a machine with the efficiency of a diesel engine, with excellent exploitation of energy. The heart is the best example of the fantastic achievements of which our muscles are capable It can, without exaggeration, be described as the best-designed engine in the world. It is easy to prove this statement. In an adult human being the heart beats 60 to 80 times a minute and about $2\frac{1}{2}$ billion times in the course of 70 years. During this space of time it drives about 260 million pints of liquid through the veins. In one single day the power engendered by this fabulous engine would suffice to raise a ton weight 59 feet in the air. The average human heart weighs only between 8 to 12 ozs., and its fuel consumption for 70 years' work could be covered by 5 cwt. of sugar. The other muscles perform similar feats, and experiments have shown that a construction of this type, by contraction, can lift a thousand times its own weight.

We know that the muscles are never completely "at rest" but are constantly in a certain state of tension, known as the tonus. On the principle of an extended spring, the muscle is ready for work at all times—in other words, it contracts on the receipt of an "order" from the brain.

But how does this contraction work? It is one of the most difficult problems that physiologists have to investigate. When we make the slightest movement, such as winking an eye or wrinkling the forehead, very complicated chemical and physical processes take place at lightning speed. Minute rod-shaped fibres of muscle protein take part, absorbing energy to a certain extent on orders and setting the spring in motion. It was previously thought that this was due to purely chemical processes, but there is some doubt about it today. The electrically-given order for the muscle to contract seems to alter the electron pattern of the atoms and subsequently the molecules involved. Energy is absorbed, directed on its way and used for work, the molecules form new groupings, and, by a close interplay of chemical and electric events, the contraction of the muscle follows. How this happens in detail has not yet been explained.

THE QUESTION OF NUTRITION

Living creatures can exist only if they have the necessary foodstuffs at their disposal. Within a larger framework this does not differ from the functioning of the muscles, which are constantly in need of fuel. Physiologically speaking, human life is a continuous metabolic process. The claims of an organism to energy-giving food corresponding to its weight, the work demanded of it and the climate, etc., are naturally very divergent. The necessary energy can be derived from the most varied foodstuffs because these provide, on a reciprocal basis, the appropriate calories (heat units) in each case. Thus, 100 grammes of protein correspond to 100 grammes of carbohydrate but only to 44·1 grammes of fat, whose calorie content is particularly high.

This concept of substitution only holds good for energy production: a purely quantitative interpretation of nutrition would be quite wrong. Indeed, our body builds itself up like any other, replacing used matter and synthesising the food absorbed in a host of complicated processes. In the case of aged or ageing animals or men, assimilation needs, which naturally play their greatest part during growth, must be taken into account. But in all other phases of life the constant renewals in the body demand the necessary "material". The outer skin must constantly be renewed, and this applies equally to the red and white blood corpuscles or the digestive juices. Everything in Nature is in constant flux, subject to constant "rebuilding". From birth to death the organism is in a state of "fluid balance", whereby the form is preserved but the building materials are perpetually renewed. With the single exception of the nerve cells, which are not renewed, every part of our body throughout its whole life is subject to continual changes in its substance. The intake material has to deliver "nourishment", which must be evaluated quantitatively, materially and in terms of energy.

Foodstuffs may be divided roughly into three groups—proteins, carbohydrates and fats. In addition to these water, salt and vitamins play an indispensable part. Proteins are mainly composed of nitrogen, which is needed by the body principally for metabolism. Since carbohydrates and fats contain no nitro-

gen they can never, on their own, fulfil nutritive needs, however great their calorie content may be. The periods of food
shortage during and after the two world wars demonstrated
this only too tragically. Countless people suffered serious de-
terioration in their health, which could primarily be traced
back to the lack of protein-rich foods. The body needs certain
specific proteins, and if these are lacking in the food an otherwise satisfactory protein intake is inadequate. This is due to the
very differing "biological values" of proteins—in other words,
to their content of the vital amino-acids.

The body can by no means assimilate the animal or vegetable
proteins in food direct, but breaks them down during digestion
to their basic particles, the amino-acids, and uses this material
for the rebuilding of the necessary individual proteins. A direct
assimilation of proteins is impossible.

Some amino-acids are not so important, while others are
necessary but can be built up by the body itself. The body cannot produce half the so far recognised amino-acids and has to
rely on their delivery, with the respective proteins, in food. We
talk therefore of essential amino-acids. If they are lacking in
the food, the organism resorts to consuming its own parts. It has
been observed in the case of the salmon that, during its long
journey to the fresh water spawning grounds, it absorbs no food
but develops very large sex glands. It occurs primarily at the
expense of its own muscle substance, which is partially "melted"
—i.e. broken down to the amino-acids and used again for the
building of new body substance (sex glands). In starving human
beings, too, their vital protein need is covered in the first place
by the musculature, whereas the heart and brain, even in extreme states of famine, are hardly touched.

Under normal conditions an ordinary mixed diet provides
the body with the necessary proteins, but individual protein
needs depend on such factors as physical weight, age and the
nature of professional activity. It has been calculated that an
adult in a temperate climate needs daily 1 gramme of protein
per kilo of physical weight. Higher figures are needed in the
case of children and pregnant and feeding mothers. In any case,
one must be careful of old-fashioned mistakes in reckoning—
thinking only in terms of calories and output requirements.
Modern diatetics have shown that the over-simplified equation

protein = protein is false. The highest biological value is to be found in the proteins of milk, meat, fish and hen's eggs; then follow soya beans, peas, rice, potatoes and oats. In animal proteins the content of vital amino-acids usually exceeds that of vegetable proteins, but the need can be supplied by the following combinations, which, according to the researches of Professor Lang, provide a balance.

Meat, eggs or milk combined with cereals.
Milk and potatoes.
Meat, eggs or milk combined with leguminous fruits.

A complete supply of protein needs is hardly possible from plants, and modern dietetics, despite many differences on individual questions, take the view that in the human diet about a third of the protein needs should be provided by animal proteins. Whether this third is obtained from meat or, as vegetarians prefer, from milk, milk products and eggs, makes very little difference in the physiology of food.

But what about the extreme vegetarians who reject any form of animal protein? One should examine the important problems of food without emotion or preconceived ideas. They are difficult enough from the purely professional standpoint. Whether a certain form of diet is right or wrong can be determined only after exact and long-term experiments on men and "guinea-pigs". No progress is possible with slogans and unproved theories. Scientifically we can only say as follows on the subject of protein needs. Man, on the basis of his digestive organs, stands somewhere between the meat and plant eaters. His bite has the typical molars of the herbivore and the incisors of the carnivore, but not the latter's canines. The length of colon lies somewhere between the corresponding organs of the above groups. As opposed to the ruminants, our body has no special apparatus for dealing with highly indigestible vegetable foods. If the strict vegetarian insists upon observing a pure vegetable diet, rejecting all animal products such as milk, eggs, etc., he will, in the course of time, inevitably overstrain his digestive organs since his diet will be lacking in vital amino-acids. This must in the long run lead to damage due to protein starvation, whether it manifests itself early or later. Very often undernourishment takes the form of some defect, such as increased susceptibility to certain infectious diseases or premature signs of ageing.

On the other hand, it must be stated quite frankly that an exaggerated consumption of meat in the diet can be equally harmful. Intensive research in the Argentine has shown that the constant consumption of animal protein has a shortening effect on life. Until recently the population of that land of great cattle herds subsisted almost solely on meat—their daily intake far surpassed that of all other civilised countries. The Minister for Health recently started a publicity campaign there with the object of warning people against their "normal" form of diet. It was proved that the average life-span of the Argentinians was far below that pertaining in other comparable lands. The main cause was found to be a one-sided diet, and the public was encouraged to eat more vegetables and fruit than before.

Extreme vegetarianism and extreme preference for animal protein are to be avoided on purely physiological grounds. A diet should be a well-balanced mixture of all the nutriments necessary for the body, and if this is not fulfilled harm is caused in the long run. Over-consumption of fatty foods is equally deleterious. Naturally neither the animal nor the human body can do without them, for fats have many different tasks to fulfil. Among these are protection against cold, the production of energy in a particularly concentrated and rapidly usable form, and participation in the building up of the body substance and the fatty reserves for emergencies such as sickness or malnutrition. The heat value of fats is high, for 1 gramme produces on an average 9·4 calories. The principal sources of our vegetable fats are nuts and cereals, which form them out of carbohydrates. Animal fats are partially formed in this way; others stem direct from the animals' food. The rapid transformation of carbohydrates—in the main sugar and starch—into fat often causes trouble to people who like sweet things. In actual fact they can be changed so swiftly and completely that these two food items can replace each other.

Protein is quite another matter, for it cannot be replaced by other items. A man can live for a long time without fats if he has enough carbohydrates at his disposal. Conversely the Eskimos, for example, can live for several months on end with practically no vegetable food. This does not harm them because a part of the rich content of fat in their food is transformed into the necessary carbohydrates. Normally the blood contains a constant proportion of fat, from which the organs take what they need. The additional fatty reserves we have already mentioned are stored in certain parts of the body, above all in the subcutaneous tissue and in the abdominal cavity. This can easily be demonstrated by experiments on animals. If a dog is fed on a fat which is easy to trace chemically, it will be found after some time in the fatty reserve depots noted above.

Until recently doctors and dieticians were gravely suspicious of all animal fats, as they seemed to be the cause of arteriosclerosis and the dreadful myocardial infarction. It was discovered that the arteries of such patients had lost their elasticity because an animal fat, cholesterol, had formed in large quantities on the inner walls. This fact is still uncontested, but it has recently been shown that the former explanation of the process rested on an error.

It is not the excessive fat in the diet that leads to hardening of the arteries: the actual cause is a disturbance in the metabolism. This gives rise to an over-production of cholesterol, with all its inherent dangers. The process can have various origins—for example, dangerously high blood pressure—but in very many cases it is not caused in the first place by a malady but by a faulty diet. Modern man is inclined to eat in too concentrated a form—above all, a lot of meat and fats and little vegetable foods. This does him no harm if his body gets the necessary exercise—if he is a manual worker or goes in for sport—but without such an expenditure of energy there is the danger of over-feeding, which is a very common occurrence today.

Modern man drives a car or takes some other form of transport, he sits at an office desk or stands by a machine, but when does he take any exercise? Lack of movement is not so harmful in youth as at a later age, when the metabolising processes slow down and the risk of a deposit of cholesterol in the arteries increases. Older men with a "paunch" generally have little desire to move about a lot or to play games. The heart is fully occupied looking after their oversized bodies, and physical effort is unwelcome. It is a dangerous condition which can be rectified only if they check their weight in time, if they take off those "extra pounds"—either by a change of diet or by sport, massage, etc. Any heavyweight who feels no inclination to follow such a course should bear in mind that research has shown quite clearly that in men over fifty an average over-weight of 15% increases mortality by more than 20%.

The contention that cancer is caused by our unnatural food is complete nonsense. The much-discussed butteryellow dye (its use in foods has been forbidden in Germany since 1938) has led only to liver tumours in rats and not in other animals, so it is doubtful whether it could cause cancer in human beings. Its ban was but a precautionary measure, since experiments with this product can naturally not be carried out on human beings. A genuine increase in cancer—doubtless the effect of urban civilisation—is shown only in cancer of the lungs and the bronchial tubes. Other forms of cancer, due to changes which take place in old age, have not shown any increase in the last thirty years. Cancer is specifically a disease of the aged, and now that more people than before reach advanced ages, the overall figures of cancer cases must inevitably rise. To this must be added the fact that formerly many types of cancer in old people were not recognised. When such patients died the cause was given as "old age".

Finally, is caries a disease brought on by civilisation? Yes and No. Decayed teeth can be found in the dinosaurs and in Stone Age man, but in modern times the disease has assumed far greater proportions. The fault, as is often maintained, is not due specifically to sugar but to potatoes, bread and in fact all the carbohydrates we absorb in our diet. However, since we cannot live without them, it is a question of finding some means of making the teeth resistant to caries. Possibly fluorine is the answer, but this has not yet been fully established.

THE GREEN PLANT FOOD FACTORY

The actual basis of the existence of all life on earth rests on the masterly achievements of vegetable chemistry. As we know, every organism constantly uses up energy which must be con-stantly renewed. Men and animals have to rely for their food entirely on plants, in which solar energy is stored. When we eat vegetables or a piece of meat from some plant-eating ani-mal, which comes to the same thing, our bodies, by breaking up this food, release the original solar energy captured by the plant and use it to a certain extent as fuel. If all the plants were to die, it would mean the end of life on earth in the shortest possible time, for they alone possess the secret of transforming the energy of the sun's rays into "mass-produced" food. Incidentally it should be noted in this context that we use the accumulated energy of primeval plants in our stoves in the form of peat, coal, etc. But how does the green plant perform this difficult chemical feat? Attempts have been made to reproduce the process in the laboratory, but the results proved pathetic when compared with the achievements of any ordinary tree. As the most important pillar in this surprising chemistry the plant uses chlorophyll, a very intricate compound whose task is to absorb the radiated light energy and then to give it off again in the form of chemical energy. Chlorophyll aids the "assimilation" of plants, in other words the formation of carbohydrates from carbon dioxide and water: the most important chemical reaction known to life is thus rendered possible. Thanks to the pioneer work of the German chemist, Professor Willstätter, we know at last the chemical structure of chlorophyll. The surprising fact came to light that the green colouring matter of the plant and the red colouring matter of blood bear a striking resemblance to each other. For the reader who is interested in chemistry we must mention that both materials contain porphyrin salts. In chlorophyll it is a magnesium salt and in hæmoglobin an iron compound. Both materials are of a very complex structure, and individually they show certain differences, but they are closely related chemically.

How does the green plant produce, from "valueless" raw materials such as carbon dioxide and water, such valuable foodstuffs as starch, sugar, etc.? That it transforms the radiated energy into chemical energy is clear. It happens in a sequence of involved processes in which numerous ferments play a part, each of them regulating certain stages of the conversion as they fall due. We cannot imitate this astounding performance on the part of the green plant, but we are at least beginning to understand the basic principles. Apparently this photosynthesis (also known as assimilation) is a combination of two completely different groups of reaction. The first leads to the building of highly complicated materials—the proto-

nutriment upon which all animals and humans rely—but the organic substance thus formed with the aid of solar energy does not remain wholly preserved: part of it is burned up again during the night. In this second reaction, which represents the respiration of the plant, oxygen is consumed and thus additional energy is won, as is the case in all forms of combustion.

The end-effect of the reactions that take place in daylight and in darkness leads to an almost perfect energetic process, for the energy for "respiration" is also produced during the light reaction, when a converse gas exchange takes place. Professor Warburg, to whom science owes important advances in this field, revealed the following facts from relevant experiments. If the energy exploitation in the processes here involved is measured accurately with green algæ the result is a utilisation of 90% radiated energy. That is a far better result than any man-made machine is capable of achieving.

There are still several points to be clarified, but basically the long-contested problem appears to have been solved. The combined effect of two completely different methods of obtaining energy—the building-up reaction in daylight and the breaking-down reaction in darkness—leads to those extraordinarily favourable results of photosynthesis which for a long time no one was able to explain. Certain phases can be recognised as ordinary syntheses, but the whole lies in the realm of higher physics and chemistry conceived by the genius of living Nature.

THE LIVING MOTOR

Let us imagine an engine which could run at will on diesel oil, petrol or coal. It would be very practical, but unfortunately the building of such a wonder engine is out of the question. The living organism, however, performs this type of remarkable feat without a thought—in a metaphoric sense of course. We have already discussed the "combustion value" of food, and are therefore fully justified in comparing the body with an engine. It needs fuel so that heat, muscular strength, and other forms of energy can be produced. We know today that all living creatures, ranging from the most primitive to man, use a basically uniform principle for the conversion of food. The chemical organisation—for the organism is virtually a chemically functioning engine—is also basically the same in all forms of life. Only in detail are various methods of solution used in reaching the same goal. The latent uniformity of the basic plan was previously overlooked in the multiplicity of the methods.

But how does this living machine function? As we have seen, it assimilates, chemically, the most varied foodstuffs with the same end-result—that all the body cells are provided with the necessary "fuel". Nature fulfils this difficult task first, by allowing the foods to be dissolved into their basic particles. Very little energy is released because to obtain it at this first stage—in view of the disparity of the materials—is too complicated and therefore too problematical for the organism. Not until later, in the course of the breaking-down processes and with the aid of the oxygen conveyed by respiration, will the chemically treated "fuel" and the ferments be drawn in for the delivery of the main part of the energy required. Hundreds of completely different reactions, preparatory to this process, are being steered uniformly towards the same goal.

This brilliantly simple organisation for the extraction of energy, with only a few end-stages, is far more practical than would be the case if each individual foodstuff were to be consumed direct and by separate methods. Whether we eat soup or salad, steak or sweet, all these very different items will first of all be "prepared" for the body, that is to say broken down into tiny basic forms rich in energy. The procedure can be illustrated by an example from hydro-electric technology. Were we to use the water of a slowly-flowing river for a turbine, or some such device, it would prove very costly and inefficient. A dam, however, and the use of a torrent over a short distance would produce the electricity far more efficiently. The organism works on a similar principle by converting the concentrated energy in a few final stages, at the end of the metabolic processes, with greater intensity.

The energy won from food is used for "heating", that is for preserving the balance of the body temperature. The running of the body is kept in balance; the muscles receive their "power" and can function; in short, the motor runs at full speed. What happens now to the fuel; how is the energy contained in food used to the best purpose? Since the body cannot work like a motorcar, which burns petrol direct, it has first to "digest" the foodstuffs. This is a complicated chemical process in which not only numerous organs but those "reaction hasteners", the ferments, take part, working on the principle of catalysis. *Inter alia* they have the task of making the food absorbed soluble in water, for this is the only way the body can cope with it. The ferments enter into loose associations with the various foodstuffs, which decompose, leaving the catalysts free once more. They can then resume their "destructive" work on further molecules, and only a very few of them need be present.

The breaking up of the macro-molecules follows in stages through the agency of several ferments, which go into action one after another. To a certain extent their effects overlap, providing additional control over the proper functioning of the digestive organs. This interplay of ferments is one of life's greatest feats. It is incredibly complicated and yet effective, safe and practical. Space prevents a detailed analysis, and we must confine ourselves to giving a hint as to the way in which Nature solves the most insuperable problems. In order to bring about the required course of the reactions, each ferment works specifically—i.e. it intervenes only at a certain prescribed point in the chemical process. Once its task is performed, it hands over the broken-down food molecules to the next ferment, and so on. A complex system of nervous stimuli and hormone effects regulates the excretion of the various digestive juices, chemical aids being used. No chemist, however, could ever hope to emulate Nature's achievements in this field.

But how does the body manage to digest the molecules of foreign protein brought in with the food without attacking its own similarly constituted substances? This is the old question: why do not the stomach or the intestines digest themselves? A chemical trick is used here. The ferments, whose influence would harm the actual cell components, are produced in a harmless inactive form in the particular cells that generate them: they are as yet proferments, which are then transformed into ferments outside the cells. Thus the ferments of the gastric juice pepsin originate from the proferment pepsinogen with the aid of the hydrochloric acid in the gastric juice. The ferments of the pancreas are activated first in the duodenum by the bile. Once more the ferments do not damage the intestinal cells because, on account of their colloidal form, they cannot penetrate these cells. Nor will the mucous membranes of the stomach wall and the respective body cells be attacked.

Many scientists are of the opinion that the wall cells of the stomach and intestine produce anti-ferments to oppose the digestive ferments. One thing is certain: only the living and fully operative wall cells are protected from the danger of being digested. If they are damaged by cutting off the blood flow, the stomach or the intestinal wall, at this particular spot, will be virtually digested by the ferments. There is, incidentally, a disease in which the pancreatic ferments become active inside the organ, leading to the "suicide" of the gland, whose living cells are digested as a result of the ferments. People contracting this disease invariably die within a few weeks.

VITAMINS ARE NECESSARY

Man has known for a long time that his food has to contain the previously mentioned materials, but unfortunately a final group of vital nutritive constituents remained completely unknown until a few decades ago. We are referring of course to the vitamins. They were first discovered because certain diseases could obviously be traced back to faulty dieting, since they were partially or wholly cured by a change of diet. Seafarers, for example, knew that on long voyages the normal ship's fare caused the dreaded scurvy. As early as the 17th century the East India Company included apples and lemons in the rations of their crews. They were found to prevent scurvy, and today we know the reason. Like rickets, beri-beri and pellagra, scurvy is numbered among the so-called deficiency diseases caused by the lack of certain vitamins in the food. Disturbances in growth, sterility and miscarriage (abortion), can also result.

All these often serious deficiency diseases can be prevented or cured if the vitamins lacking are made up with fruit, vegetables, milk, cod liver oil, etc. Today we know a great number of vitamins but certainly not all, for new ones are constantly being discovered.

Exactly like ferments and hormones, vitamins work in the smallest quantities on the principle of catalysts and, with these two other agents, play a large part in the regulation of the life processes. Like ferments, they also have a "first stage," when,

THE FUNCTIONS OF LIFE

as such, they are harmless. The body activates the first stage of Vitamin A, carotene, in the liver, thus rendering it an effective agent. The first stage of the anti-rachitic Vitamin D, ergosterin, is activated by ultra-violet radiation.

A long-contested question, why rickets can be healed both by direct administration of Vitamin D and by ultra-violet treatment has thus been clarified. The ergosterin is situated in the human skin and becomes effective by solar or artificial ultra-violet radiation. In practice it is important to realise that certain vitamins, such as the B Group, can be destroyed by cooking. As a result of their solubility in water they can be lixiviated. When vegetables are left to cook for a long time and the water is poured away, a great part of their nutritive value disappears down the sink. Not only are the vitamins lost by this lixiviation, but also all the nourishing salts and trace elements. Vegetables should always be steamed for a short time with little water. This is far cheaper and more practical than buying synthetically produced vitamins at the chemist's.

In addition to the organic nutriments and vitamins, the organism has a constant need of a certain amount of minerals, without which it cannot exist. Every living cell contains inorganic salts, which it uses for building and for maintaining a balanced course of all functions. It needs these as much as the actual energy-producing nutriments of an organic nature. Primarily the salts serve, in very distinct proportions, as building-blocks for tissue.

If we weigh the ash of burnt body substances and measure their salt content by the normal analytic method, we find that dental enamel gives 96·4% salt, bone 65·4%, cartilage 34% and muscle 5%. Further, the salts participate in the preservation of the "right" (i.e. the weak alkaline) reaction of the blood; and finally the formation of the blood and the hormones are dependent upon minerals.

Although most salts are supplied in sufficient quantities in a normal diet, man also needs sodium chloride or common salt. He shares this need with many herbivores such as sheep, which are known to have a great hunger for salt, whereas the carnivores which live solely on meat have their need for salt sufficiently catered for. The more the diet of man is confined to vegetable foods, the greater will be his need for cooking salt, and vice-versa. Agricultural peoples, from time immemorial, have salted their foods, whereas hunting folk never do. Undoubtedly cooking salt is far more than a method of making a dish more tasty; modern dietetics have shown that the two main components of cooking salt, chlorine and sodium, are essential to life. Various scientists have proved, by experiments on themselves, that lack of salt in the food brings about a decline in their physical and mental faculties. In extreme cases, when working in great heat, with the corresponding loss of salt by perspiration, an insufficient replacement of this mineral can lead to fatal phenomena, such as heart failure following serious cramp. These heat cramps can be cured in a very short time by administering common salt.

The reason for the great importance of sodium chloride can be referred to here only in brief. It passes with great ease through the cell membranes, thereby ensuring a constant balance between cations and anions in the cells and body juices. Vegetable food is particularly rich in potassium but poor in sodium, and this is why the vegetarian needs more cooking salt than the meat-eater in order to maintain a balance in his mineral economy. Only in special cases, in the treatment of certain diseases, is a diet poor or entirely lacking in salt necessary.

Calcium is used primarily for the building up and preservation of the skeleton, in which 99% of the whole calcium content of the body is found. Food poor in calcium leads to insufficient calcification of the bones, but the nervous system will also be affected and nervous disturbances will result. Calcium actually has the effect of reducing the irritability of the nerves and incidentally of the muscles. The anti-rachitic vitamin D plays a part in the balanced intake of calcium by the body, along with certain fats, fatty acids and hormones. The actual regulation of the calcium metabolism lies with a special hormone formed by the accessory thyroids, which sees that a certain prescribed calcium content is maintained in the blood. If it sinks below normal, cramps result—a condition known as tetany.

Closely associated with calcium metabolism is that of phosphorus, and the necessary amounts of these salts are mutually determined. A calcium deficiency in food is therefore doubly disadvantageous, a fact which should be constantly borne in mind. The adult needs 0·8 gm. to 1 gm. of calcium daily. Pregnant women and children, on the other hand, need nearly three times as much. The supply from food presents certain difficulties, since calcium is only present in large quantities in a very few foodstuffs which are not always obtainable. As a result there is a general calcium deficiency, greater in fact than is generally supposed.

When we think that countless vital physical functions are dependent upon the calcium content of the blood and tissues, directly and indirectly, we can understand the demand of many dieticians to ensure, by every means, an optimal satisfaction of calcium needs. In various countries this has been achieved by adding a certain amount of calcium carbonate to bread and flour. This measure seems to be paying dividends.

Similar measures were recently taken regarding another inorganic component of food—iron. It is needed for building hæmoglobin and various ferments and is found in most body cells. A lack of this metal can prevent a satisfactory renewal of red blood corpuscles and finally lead to anæmia. To prevent this there is a law in the United States that bread must contain an adequate amount of ferrous salts. Young people, and pregnant and feeding mothers need 15 mg. to 20 mg. of iron per day, whereas adults can be satisfied completely with 8 mg. to 10 mg., but they absorb far more than this in their normal diet. Scientists are not yet agreed whether too little or too much iodine in food and water is responsible for the well-known disturbances in gland functioning such as Basedow's disease, myxedema and goitre. The dispensing of pure salt containing iodine for the prevention of goitre also meets with mixed verdicts. All other minerals, such as bromine, sulphur, phosphorus and magnesium, are to be had in sufficient quantities in normal food and therefore need no discussion.

In the case of animals the same principles apply. They, too, break up their food with the help of ferments, absorb it in the intestines, and convert it into body substance and fuel. Individually there are so many variations of this great theme in the animal world that it would be impossible to enumerate them all. There are the countless parasites that feed on the blood of other animals or live in the bodies of their hosts, taking their food directly through the skin, as for example the tape worm. Other animals, again, like the snake, never chew but merely swallow their prey in a single lump, thanks to the enormous expansion capacity of their gullets. Spiders suck their victims after injecting digestive fluid into their bodies.

Starfish are particularly subtle, and one of their favourite foods is the succulent oyster. Despite all resistance, they prise open the shells with the aid of their tentacles and pour their digestive juices through the chink on to the oyster. After some time it is "digested", and the starfish can drink it as fluid. Carnivores, with their concentrated diet, have a comparatively short intestine. In plant-eaters it is considerably longer, while in the case of ruminants there is a special section of the stomach (the paunch) where the predigestion of cellulose takes place with the aid of bacteria. These useful bacteria are instrumental in producing the necessary ferments.

Caterpillars of moths and butterflies, on the other hand, are not in this fortunate position, nor have they any ferments of their own to break up the cellulose in their vegetable diet, a fact which is by no means a matter of indifference to man, for it is the reason why caterpillars have to eat such enormous quantities and sometimes cause extensive damage to our woods. Anyone who has bred silkworms will know from experience what bad food-converters these larvæ are, simply because they lack ferments. From hatching to pupation they need such quantities of mulberry leaves that their weight corresponds to five thousand times the weight of their cocoon.

"BLOOD IS A VERY SPECIAL JUICE"

This famous remark by Mephistopheles is very true, not in any mystical but in a purely physiological sense. Actually the red juice of life of which an adult possesses 9 to 12 pints, is the most complicated "exhibit" in the amazing laboratory of Nature. It is composed of every conceivable acid, base, salt and nutriment, besides the secretions of the endocrine glands and many other substances. In blood all organs find the nourishment for their special function—the material for building new cells or the renewal of old tissue. Everything depends upon the right co-operation of tissue and organs with the blood —health or disease, physical strength or weakness, and, in the last analysis, life or death. Nutrients and metabolic waste, oxygen and carbonic acid, are all transported in its stream, and finally, with the help of special police cells, it affords protection against the assaults of bacteria.

In many of the lower animals the intestine takes over the distribution of food through the body direct, whereas higher life has developed particular channels, the blood vessels, in the course of its evolution. The vertebrates possess a perfectly enclosed vascular system, a true blood circulatory system. This consists of the heart (pumping apparatus) in addition to the arteries, veins and capillaries. To be accurate, we have two pumps—one for the general or systemic circulation, which carries the blood through the whole organism, and one for the pulmonary circulation, which leads through the lungs. Anatomically these two pumps form a single unit and each consists of an auricle and a ventricle. The left pump serves the general circulation and therefore has more work to do than the right, and for this reason the left side of our heart is more powerfully built than the right side.

Here again Nature works in the most economic way possible. The bloodflow rate in our bodies is never constant, for all our organs could not run at full speed at the same time. This is evident from the well-known tiredness we may experience after a big meal. We become lazy physically and mentally, a sign that the digestive organs have claimed large proportions of blood and that the muscles and brain are consequently not supplied with as much as usual. Conversely, with the aid of sensitive test apparatus, it was found that the solution of a difficult mathematical calculation was accompanied by a very small reduction of flow in the arm. The brain needed a great deal of blood, and the extremity received slightly less. The heart is very dependent upon the cerebrum and is therefore affected by emotion. It beats even faster during a difficult "exam" or some excitement than it does under heavy physical effort.

One of the most important tasks of the blood is to provide the whole body with vital oxygen and thus to keep the "combustion engine of the body" running. In order to understand the mechanics of this operation we must take a brief look at the composition of our life juice. It is not uniform liquid such as water, but consists of two groups of particles—a liquid basic substance, the blood plasma, and the cellular particles. Of the latter there are three different types, the red and the white blood corpuscles (erythrocytes and leukocytes) and the blood platelets (thrombocytes). The iron-containing hæmoglobin is largely the vehicle for conveying oxygen to the cells. Such an aid is necessary, for only a small percentage of oxygen dissolves in liquid and the body, without the help of hæmoglobin, would never be able to take in sufficient quantities however intense the respiration. Hæmoglobin binds the oxygen loosely to itself by chemical means, forwards it to the necessary part of the body and releases it by a breakdown of this combination (oxy-hæmoglobin).

At each heartbeat the blood is driven from the right half of the heart—the heart is divided by a vertical wall—into the pulmonary system, while at the same time blood flows out of the larger left half into the general system. In order to prevent it flowing back by contraction of the ventricles, there are the two cunningly-built cardiac valves (their presence enables a doctor to detect any malfunction or valvular defect). The blood pumped into the pulmonary system flows into the capillaries of the lungs—a fine network of arteries, which take over the exchange of material here as they do elsewhere in the body. The walls of the capillaries are so thin that the oxygen in the lungs can be absorbed by the blood, where it is seized by the hæmoglobin and "bound" in the way we have described. Next the blood comes through the pulmonary vein into the left ventricle and flows into the general system, where the red blood corpuscles deliver the oxygen to the cells, once more through the capillary walls. Since a cubic millimetre of blood contains the fantastic number of 5 million red corpuscles, delivery of oxygen is made possible to the remotest body cells in the shortest time. This is very necessary, for the amount of oxygen contained in the blood will last a man in repose only for about two minutes—a fact which explains the dire consequences that can follow even a short interruption of the heart's activity. If the unusually sensitive brain is left without blood for even a few seconds, a man immediately loses consciousness.

As it flows along the general system the blood not only conveys oxygen, foodstuffs, salts, hormones, etc., to the individual cells, but it bears away the waste products formed by the count-less processes taking place in the body. Carbon dioxide is accepted by the blood plasma and the red corpuscles. It then reaches the right half of the heart and is pumped once more into the pulmonary system, i.e. the lungs, where it gives up carbon dioxide, and the red cells are recharged with oxygen through the capillary walls.

The disposal of waste, the used proteins, is not so simple. The poisonous ammonia resulting from their chemical break-down is transformed by the liver into the hydrolytic substance, urea, but this cannot be expelled by the "exhaust pipe" of the lungs because it is not in gaseous form. The blood therefore takes over the removal and delivers it to the qualified excretory organs—the kidneys—which, among their other tasks, see to it that urea and uric acid disappear from the body. They extract these materials, together with the metabolic waste from the blood, and finally excrete them in a liquid solution, urine. A special branch of the general circulatory system, the renal arteries, comes into play in the service of waste disposal. This is the kidney circuit, which is geared in as an accessory.

A further special circuit in the body is the hepatic circuit, which supplies the liver with blood. In this versatile organ nutrients are partially stored, freed of toxins, and rebuilt. The liver receives them through the great portal vein, in which the blood vessels from the intestines unite. The distribution of nourishment to the body cells follows through the blood liquid, the plasma, which contains all the necessary mineral salts along with glucose and proteins in colloidal solution. The proteins in the plasma are of a specific nature—in other words, they differ according to the animal species. Alien protein will be con-verted in the body into its specific protein. This explains the well-known hypersensitivity to alien protein when it is intro-duced direct into the bloodstream and not through the digestive channels, as for instance by injection. One of the proteins in blood plasma, fibrinogen, has the vital task of closing damaged blood vessels by clotting. It is quite a complicated process. When a vessel is broken the blood platelets gather at the edge of the wound, disintegrate, and release a ferment, which, in combination with other constituents of the blood plasma, causes a formation known as fibrin, a fine network of needle-like fibres.

In hæomophilic subjects this combination is disturbed and their blood has very little or no capacity for clotting. Such people can sometimes bleed to death from the most trifling wounds.

POLICE OF THE BLOOD

In the blood there are "special police" in the form of the white corpuscles, which work fairly independently, their task being to defend the body from disease agents and to act as scavengers. Of these colourless cells—they are not really white —the blood contains from 5,000 to 7,000 per cubic mm. as opposed to the millions of red corpuscles. But despite this small quantity their significance is great enough. The white corpuscles constantly patrol the body and see that everything is in order. Like the amœbæ, they move with the aid of pseudopodia, can slip in anywhere, even through the capillary walls, and seek out immediately any dangerous invaders. They form their own ferments, reproduce, and work in different groups in combating disturbances.

Presumably each of these groups—there are four or five distinct types of leukocytes—fulfils its own special task. One group exudes substances to attack inopportune bacteria; another may render harmless the toxins of these diminutive enemies; and the so-called phagocytes surround bacteria and dead body cells with their pseudopodia and devour them. We can watch a battle of this nature between the "police of the blood" and bacteria in our own bodies. When, for example, we let a wound become infected, the body immediately sends its defence forces into action at the endangered spot. An increased blood flow is directed there so that the spot in question becomes red and hot—what we call inflamed. The white corpuscles start their battle with the invading bacteria and are usually the victors. Sometimes the bacteria have an initial success and destroy some of the white "police". Then pus forms, which consists merely of dead white corpuscles.

Other defence forces of the blood contained in the scrum (blood plasma without congealing material) now enter the fray and engage their chemical protective substances against the enemy. If there is any further advance, then so-called antibodies or amboceptors are formed, which render the bacterial poison harmless. In certain diseases, if this intervention of the antibodies is successful, the body remains immune to their further attack for some time, or perhaps for the rest of its life, because the antibodies remain in the blood.

Serum treatment for many diseases rests on this fact. Animals are taken and carefully injected with disease agents in order to build up defence materials. Blood is then tapped off and allowed to congeal. After a certain period the serum separates as yellow liquid containing all the antitoxins. Antiserum treatment can also be used as a prophylactic after the outbreak of a disease, but this must not be confused with protective inoculation, where the body is rendered immune by the injection of dead or weakened bacteria for the formation of antibodies. Inoculation, for example, against smallpox or typhus, is used all over the world with great success and has saved the lives of thousands.

Both red and white corpuscles continually die and must therefore be replaced. In the case of serious loss of blood the need for red corpuscles is particularly urgent, and they will be produced in large quantities from the bone marrow. Incidentally, the "cemeteries" for old or incapable cells of this type are in the spleen and the liver, and there the dead red corpuscles are broken down; their most valuable component, iron, is carefully extracted and used to form new hæmoglobin.

In addition to the blood vascular system there is a kind of liaison in the body between blood and tissue. This is the lymphatic system, in which the fluid that surrounds all the body cells collects and is circulated. Fluid constantly leaving the blood capillaries flows slowly into the small and large cavities between the cells, where it is picked up by its own lymph capillaries and, via the lymphatic system, finally reaches the bloodstream once more in the sub-clavian artery. The tissues are therefore permanently saturated with lymph and retain the fats transported by the blood. The metabolic waste of the cells is also picked up by the lymph and returned to the blood.

A very important part in the battle against invading bacteria is played by the countless lymph nodes, in which the lymphatic system has set up a kind of control post. In the nodes one of the groups of white corpuscles, the lymphocytes, is formed, and these, together with the other "police forces" of the body, serve as defence against dangerous microbes. The contest in the lymph nodes does not always result in favour of the white corpuscles. When the glands in the armpits and the groins swell and show a tendency to become inflamed it is because the lymphocytes cannot immediately overcome the invading bacteria. Everyone has had an experience of this at some time or another.

To close our brief review of the functions of the blood we must mention that the blood transfusions given with such success today nearly always proved catastrophic in olden days. Thanks to two known facts, our knowledge of the clotting processes and of the blood groups, blood transfusions today are almost without danger. In each transfusion the donor's blood is artificially prevented from clotting for a certain length of time; and the blood groups of donor and recipient are checked to avoid the clumping or agglutination of the blood cells that would result from a combination of antipathetic groups.

THE MIGHT OF THE SMALLEST UNITS

We have already seen that the living organism can carry out an uninterrupted sequence of the most complicated chemical processes beyond the powers of any chemist. The question is how the course of all these processes is regulated, so that the right sequences will lead to the right results. Undoubtedly the nervous system plays a leading role, but there must be other regulating factors, for there are countless organisms that possess no nervous system.

We know today that the biochemistry of plants, animals, and human beings is regulated in the main by the biocatalysts—hormones, vitamins and ferments. Originally these three groups were sharply differentiated, but the more we learn about them and about their effects, the clearer it becomes that they work in the closest co-operation. All three groups form an inner unit, a regulating centre as it were, for Nature never allows the same material to function in one case as a hormone and in another as a vitamin, or vice-versa. Vitamins appear as important components of ferments or activate the formation of hormones, and all the effects of such substances, vital to the whole of life, are achieved by the use of the smallest conceivable quantities. With one *thirty-millionth* of a gramme of sex-hormone clearly recognisable effects can be induced in a mouse.

In the animal kingdom and in man the hormones, as we know, are formed by the endocrine glands, organs that do not excrete their juices like the sweat glands but secrete them inside the body, direct into the bloodstream. We are familiar today with a whole series of hormones of the sex glands. We can create some of them synthetically and put them to successful use in countless disturbances and diseases of the sexual organs. Although these hormones determine the typical male and female sex characters, the woman also possesses male and the man female hormones; so that, hormonally speaking, we are bi-sexual, even if the "qualified" hormone is normally dominant. But Nature does not make nearly such sharp distinctions between male and female as it was formerly thought.

One of the hormones best known to the public is insulin. It is formed by widely separated groups of cells in the pancreas and regulates the sugar metabolism by building up glucose into glycogen and storing it in the liver. If one removes the pancreas of a dog, it will immediately become diabetic, which simply means that the carbohydrate metabolism no longer functions correctly after the removal of the regulating hormone. The sugar content in the blood rises considerably and sugar appears, contrary to plan, in the urine—even when the animal is given no more carbohydrate in its food. The sugar, therefore, originated from ill-directed building-up processes in the animal's body. Here we also have the cause of what can be a very considerable loss of weight in serious cases of diabetes. If pancreatic tissue is grafted on to the subject of our experiment, or the animal is given insulin, the sugar in the urine will disappear—at least for a short time. As a result of this knowledge we have carried out very successful treatments with insulin.

The above-mentioned interplay of biocatalysts is well illustrated by the example of insulin. It works in concert with adrenalin, a hormone that is formed in the medulla of the suprarenals. These small glands situated above the kidneys can be looked upon as "shock troops" for the body. If danger threatens, if a man or an animal comes into a dangerous situation, the adrenalin acts as an alarm signal; great quantities are released, activating all the strength for defence or flight. The effect of adrenalin is to produce a sudden rush of glucose into the bloodstream. This happens by the mobilisation of the glycogen reserves which, with the aid of insulin, have been stored in the liver.

At the same time the adrenalin takes further alarm measures: the blood vessels contract, blood pressure increases, the heart beats faster, respiration is speeded up, and at the moment of danger unnecessary activities of the digestive organs are curtailed. Adrenalin is therefore an activating hormone which reacts extensively to emotional influences (shock, excitement and fear). When we turn pale with "shock" on reading our income tax demands the adrenalin comes into play. The arterioles of the skin narrow as a result of the reduced flow of blood into them, and for this reason the face loses colour.

In the cortex of the suprarenals further hormones which perform a host of very important functions in the regulation of metabolism are produced. Underproduction of these hormones leads to physical debility, such as occurs after an attack of 'flu for example. This can often be remedied by the use of synthetically produced cortical hormones (cortisone).

We know today that the thyroid gland produces an important hormone which greatly influences physical development and metabolism as a whole. When there is a deficiency animals or men remain under-developed. Conversely, over-production leads to the well-known symptoms of Basedow's disease. This malady, recognisable by the typical exophthalmia, or protruding eyeballs, can be cured by removing part of the thyroid gland; on the other hand, insufficient production of the latter's iodine-bearing hormone (leading as we saw to under-development) can be fought with iodine preparations or the administration of additional hormone. In the millennial de-iodising process of the earth's crust iodine is brought down by the rivers to the sea, where it is more concentrated. This is possibly the reason why in mountainous regions, where the water is poor in iodine, goitre and cretinism are more widespread, whereas on the iodiferous coasts Basedow's disease is common. Another hormone, formed in the parathyroids, regulates the essential calcium metabolism of the blood and sees to it that its calcium content remains constant.

The versatile and complex regulating organisation that Nature has created in the hormones also has its leader—a "conductor" of the hormone orchestra, as a music-loving biologist once expressed it. In the pituitary (hypophysis) the remarkable achievements of the hormone apparatus reach unsurpassed heights. In this twin-lobed gland, lodged in the sphenoid bone below the brain, no less than nine different hormones are formed which regulate directly and indirectly an incalculable number of physical functions. The major tasks of this tiny gland, hardly bigger than a pea, range from procreation and growth to the contraction of the uterine musculature in childbirth.

If its most important parts, the anterior lobes, are removed from a young experimental animal, the latter's whole development is brought to a standstill and it remains a dwarf. On the other hand, if young rats are fed on the glandular substance, they will become considerably larger than normal. The activity of the pituitary is not confined to the production of hormones which in themselves give rise to the most disparate effects, although these are varied enough (growth, milk secretion, maturation of the ova, pregnancy, blood pressure, etc.); in addition to all this, its hormones guard and influence the regulating characters of the thyroid, suprarenals, pancreas and presumably other glands. Conversely, we have been able to observe in this astonishing interplay a number of reciprocal effects of the activity of other endocrine glands on the pituitary. It is certainly no coincidence that this smallest of all the glands is connected directly with the brain. If we are ever to solve the tricky problem of psycho-physical metabolism, then this tiny pituitary will surely be found to play a crucial part, but the solution is still a long way off.

The relations between hormones and vitamins are so close and varied that we shall have to confine ourselves to a few typical examples. A diet poor in vitamins, for instance, is clearly prejudicial to hormone production, the reason being that the endocrine glands have the highest vitamin need of all the organs of the body. Growing animals and men do not become sexually mature when there is a lack of vitamins, and in adults the sexual interest is extinguished. In the case of scurvy (lack of vitamin C) the hormone-forming activity of the suprarenals is disturbed to a degree dangerous to life. Vitamin C is of special significance in the whole interplay of biocatalysts. It activates both the suprarenal hormones and some of the vital ferments, and in some animals it can even function as a hormone.

Other vitamins work closely with the thyroid hormone. In instances of over-production of this biocatalyst (Basedow) they have been used successfully as a "brake" against the pathological increase in metabolism. And finally we must mention that in vitamin E we have a very necessary complement to the sex-hormones. Should this vitamin be lacking in the diet considerable disturbances in the procreative organs can ensue. Vitamin E has recently been used successfully in animal breeding as a remedy for chronic miscarriage. Intensive research is being carried out on the subject of the interplay of biocatalysts, and hardly a month passes that does not bring new results in this highly interesting field. By and large, and despite all differences, hormones, vitamins, and ferments are basically the same: they are biocatalysts, activators of life. They constantly steer life's functions and, in fact, make it possible.

BREATHING WITH AND WITHOUT LUNGS

Vital oxygen is led through the blood to the cells of our bodies. Plants and countless marine animals do not require this detour via the blood: they simply breathe through the skin. This only occurs naturally when the surface of the body is so thin that the oxygen can percolate through it. If it is too firm for this direct traffic, then special respiratory organs have to take its place. As usual, Nature has solved the problem in various different ways—by the trachea of the insects, etc., whose fistular system makes possible a direct supply of oxygen to all parts of the body by gills, and finally by lungs. In the building of these organs care has been taken to provide them with the largest surface possible, so that they can absorb a maximum of oxygen. The human lung possesses over 300 million tiny pulmonary alveoli as reception points for the gas and has a working surface of over 100 sq. yards!

In the gills of fish the enlargement of the surface is achieved by the development of countless small gill platelets. With their aid the fish absorbs the oxygen dissolved in the water in its red corpuscles on exactly the same principle as in pulmonary breathing. They, too, cannot utilise the gas until it enters the bloodstream through the capillary walls. Why then, one might ask, do so many human beings drown every year and why, on the contrary, do fish suffocate when taken out of the water? The answer lies in the different construction of the respective respiratory organs. The gills of a fish cannot function in air, and our lungs are designed for absorbing gaseous oxygen, enough of which is not contained in water. Hence the insufficient "delivery" of the vital gas in both cases. On the same grounds, the lung-breathing whale has to surface from time to time. If it possessed gills, it would be far better protected against the depredations of man.

In all land animals the lung is situated inside the body in order to protect its highly sensitive tissue. Additional safety measures ensure that the respiratory conduits—trachea and bronchial tubes—are protected from dust. To this end they are kept constantly moist by the secretions of special mucus cells, which remove the particles of dust trapped in the mucous by means of a kind of "dusting brush". This consists of a host of the finest hairs, known as ciliated epithelia, which cover the mucous membranes. They are in constant motion and work in well-defined waves, thus leading any small disturbing elements back to the mouth. Larger particles, such as crumbs of bread, are removed by a very effective protective reflex known as coughing. The respiratory movements which can ensue, more or less intensely, are regulated by the respiratory centre in the brain. It is irritated by the acid content of the blood, which is dependent above all upon carbonic acid concentrations.

But this very sensitive respiratory centre also reacts to various other influences. During strenuous physical effort the lactic acid production of the muscles increases and irritates the respiratory centre to increased activity. Respiration therefore deepens, the body cells retain more oxygen, and the living motor receives more fuel. The same results can be achieved by cooling-off the skin or subjecting it to ultra-violet rays. Through the cooling-off, the newborn baby is impelled to take its first breath. If it fails to do so of its own accord, it should be given a gentle slap on the back or carefully immersed in cold water. Emotional influences can strongly affect the respiratory centre. The expression "breathtaking suspense" is very appropriate. It has been noticed, for instance, in children that, while reading an exciting story, their breathing actually stops at the moment of the greatest tension.

Nature uses a particular trick for regulating the respiratory centre in ducks, which, although they possess lungs, can remain for a considerable time under water. By stretching its neck and head at the moment of diving the respiratory centre of the duck is temporarily arrested, and thus it can "end up" for minutes on end without any difficulties of breathing. Plants and many of the lower animals breathe through the leaves or skin, respectively, which have fissures to enable the air to enter. By day green plants produce far more oxygen by assimilation than they need for breathing, and, taken all in all, the "delivery" is far greater than the consumption. This is fortunate, for otherwise life would long since have died out on the earth for lack of this vital gas. However, not entirely, for certain living creatures—for example, yeast cells—are anærobic and can metabolise without any participation of oxygen, thanks to the ferments they build. Countless bacteria perform the same feat, and some parasites can live practically without oxygen; but they are exceptions and the greater part of the earth's inhabitants needs this gas unconditionally. As in all such processes the ferments play their part in respiration. Several respiratory ferments have been discovered—they are to be found in all the body cells, where they carry out by stages the biological oxydation which gives the body its energy.

THE SENSES AS GATEWAYS TO THE OUTSIDE WORLD

For man and animal alike the sense organs are the actual bridges to the world. Only by their aid can they experience everything necessary for living—from the "irritability responses" of the amœba to the highest forms of human knowledge. Even the plant has something in the nature of sense organs, by whose aid it reacts in a prescribed manner to certain external conditions such as light, gravity, etc. Compared with the animal, however, the plant has an easy time, for it does not have to hunt for food, but finds it on the spot. For the free-moving animals the senses play a far greater part in the struggle for existence—for procuring food, discovering enemies and finding their mates. To fulfil all these needs Nature has developed special sensory cells, which rise from primitive beginnings to an amazing complexity in the higher stages of life. This applies especially to the development of the light sense,

which we human beings rate highest of all. Many animals—
the earthworm is one—have certain sensory cells in their
bodies by whose aid they can tell whether it is light or dark.
They are adequate for these light-shy creatures.

Certain protozoa, such as the tiny euglena, have a rudimentary eye at the front of the body, the so-called eye spot. It is
composed of carotene, the same material as we find in our
visual purple. In the platyhelminthes and other lower animals
pigment alveoles develop. These aggregations of black dye
grains, which close like a cup over a group of cells susceptible
to light, are arranged on either side of the head and in this
primitive fashion a certain directional vision becomes possible.
In snails we find the slotted eye, a further improvement. Here a
great number of visual cells lie in a trench-like depression in the
head. These rudiments of a true visual organ give no picture
of the environment but merely register differences of brightness.

The next step forward is found in a type of squid, the nautilus,
one of the last descendants of the many ammonites that live in
tropical seas. Its eye is built on the principle of the pinhole
camera. The rays of light pass through a narrow opening in
the forepart of the eye and fall upon a layer susceptible to light,
the retina, where a number of visual cells are herded together in
a very narrow space. In the pinhole camera, of course, a
photographic plate occupies a like position to the retina. As in
this long-since outmoded camera, the resultant picture on the
retina of the nautilus is very weak in light because few rays can
pass through the narrow aperture.

Modern photographic technique has rectified the defect by
placing a lens in the "eye aperture" of the camera. Its task is
to break up the entering light rays and to unite them in a sharp
bright picture on a plate or film. Nature has used exactly the
same technique from time immemorial in the case of the lens-
eye. In approaching this very interesting problem one has the
impression that she experimented with the eyes of living
creatures. Having created the not particularly successful pinhole camera eye of the nautilus, she then gave the arthropods—
still experimentally, so to speak—a combination of several
single eyes which unite to project a picture. Many insects
can receive quite sharp pictures with their faceted eyes. She
abandoned this line of development and, alongside other

phyla such as worms and molluscs, gave the highest representatives of life on earth, the vertebrates, a lens-eye which seems to have reached the height of perfection.

NATURE'S GREATEST WORK OF ART

Let us examine somewhat more closely the eye of the vertebrate, an organ which has fascinated the greatest minds, and not only those of scientists. Men such as Dürer, Leonardo da Vinci, Goethe and Helmholtz devoted a large part of their lives to studying this natural masterpiece. Today we know far more about the eye than any other organ of the human or animal body, and yet our knowledge is far from complete, for its most important working methods still remain a matter of hypothesis. At first sight its construction seems easy to understand. The eye consists of various transparent refracting layers —cornea, aqucous humor, crystalline lens and vitreous body— through which the light must travel before striking the retina. These form the optical apparatus, which breaks the rays, concentrates them, and projects a picture of the outside world sharply on the "photographic plate" of the eye.

Here in the retina lie the sensory cells susceptible to light and colour, the so-called rods and cones. They are irritated by the incoming rays; the stimuli collect in the visual nerves and are carried to the centre of sight in the cortex of the cerebrum. With its thick optic nerve, the retina is basically no more than a particularly fine membrane sensitive to light, an outpost of the brain, separated from the outside world by a transparent window. In the service of the retina are countless apparatuses which have special tasks to perform and can go into action according to requirements. In bright daylight we use completely different retina elements from those used in twilight or in the dark. The "dimming apparatus" of the eye cannot be switched on and off with the lightning speed of an electric lamp, but gradually adapts itself to increased demands. In the dark a red pigment, visual purple, is produced which greatly increases the eye's sensitivity to light. After half an hour our night vision has become a thousand times more sensitive.

The reason we see colours is because certain chemical materials in the cones of the retina are stimulated by individual waves of light. Purely daylight animals such as lizards possess almost exclusively cones, or "daylight vision cells", in their retina. The same applies to most birds, which are blind after dusk. Nocturnal animals, on the contrary, are in the main equipped with rods which are insensitive to colour and, in compensation, they have large quantities of visual purple at their disposal.

In men and apes the combined effect of having the two eyes focused ahead provides binocular vision with a field in relief, whereas in most other mammals, with their eyes set to the side of the head, a reduced binocular field results. The relief picture, achieved by the coalescing of the views projected on the retina by both eyes, gives us the spatial distance of objects in correct perspective.

The eye accepts only a very small section of the spectrum as light, viz. the wavelengths between 800 and 400 millimicrons (red to violet). From experiments on animals we know that not only mammals and birds, but also insects such as bees and butterflies, can see in colour despite their differently-constructed eyes. Bees, however, do not see rays which to us are red, but on the other hand they can see ultra-violet light.

Part of the technical apparatus of the eye is the iris, which works like the diaphragm of a camera, facilitating adaptation to changing light conditions. Sharpness is achieved by rapidly curving the frontal surfaces of both lenses according to optical need. This is a far better arrangement than the rigid glass lens of our cameras. A practical and very important characteristic of the retina is its so-called inertia. When a light irritation strikes the retina there is a short time lag before it takes effect: we also think we are still seeing a light when in fact there is no light. This tardiness of the eye has made possible the triumph of cinematography. When we look at a film the series of pictures combine into a single picture because the inertia of the eye does not allow us to separate the individual pictures from each other.

The same principle applies to many optical illusions of everyday life, such as when we see single drops of rain as "shafts", or a rotating propeller as a "disc". These phenomena are traceable to the same cause: the eye cannot take in light impressions of less than one-sixteenth of a second's duration. Below this figure, as Uexküll says, "time stands still". Other phenomena of this type come under the heading of irradiation.

Because of the inertia of the retina unusually strong reflections are afforded by white objects; a white shoe, for instance, makes the foot appear larger. The eye sees black objects in very sharp contours, whereas white contours are hazy, and one practical result of this slight optical "defect" is of great aid to every woman. She knows that a black dress will make her look slimmer, while white will have the opposite effect.

THE TRIUMPH OF SENSITIVITY

In newspaper reports we often read of people achieving something remarkable with the aid of a sixth sense, such as clairvoyance. Such reports are based on the outdated view that men and animals possess only five known senses. Actually we have far more senses than sight, hearing, smell, taste and touch, for there are three more sensory units in our skin alone. In addition to the familiar sense of touch there are in the skin special hot and cold receptors and pressure points distributed unevenly over the whole body. There are, for example, certain main regions such as the conjunctiva of the eye, which only registers cold, whereas the eyelid reacts strongly to heat. Over the whole cutaneous surface there are about 250,000 cold points and 30,000 warm points. They are sensitive to the slightest change of temperature, and this is far more important to us than is generally suspected. The entire regulation of our body heat is largely influenced by them, including blood distribution and even our subjective feeling of well being. Only at a time when neither the cold nor the warm points is "signalling" do we feel really comfortable. Physiologists speak of a "zone of comfort", meaning the temperature region within which no neural commands for heat regulation are given by the skin. The hands and knees are comparatively insensitive. On the other hand, the warm and cold points of the facial skin are particularly dense round the forehead. This can be proved quite simply by taking off one's hat while out walking: the sudden sense of coolness is due to the bare forehead coming in contact with an almost continuous draught of air.

A fourth cutaneous sense, the sense of pain, is localised at many—in fact a vast number—of points. It will react strongly even at the prick of a needle. To be more accurate, it is only a partial zone of the sense of pain, for in certain circumstances

A praying mantis, so called because of its curious posture. The photograph shows quite clearly the sharp claws, the dangerous weapons of this robber insect.

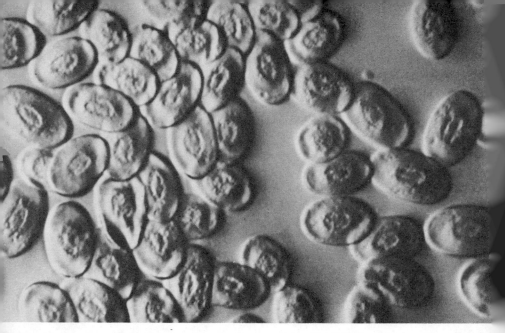

Blood corpuscles of a frog (enlarged 1,500 times).

Human blood corpuscles (enlarged 2,000 times).

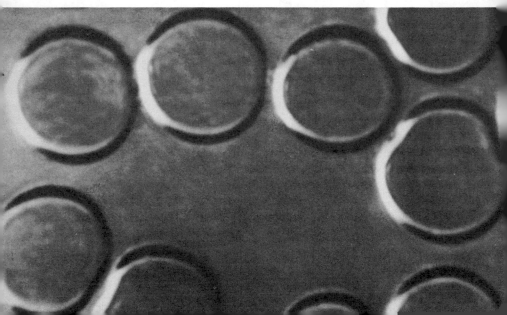

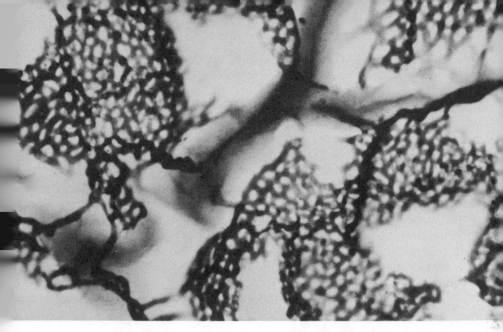

Human lung utricles (enlarged 120 times).

Villi of the small intestine. They enlarge the surface of the intestinal mucus, thus improving its digestive effect.

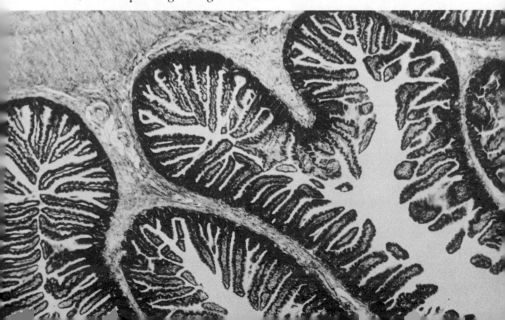

The stings of the nettle, a primitive form of defense in the plant kingdom (enlarged 35 times).

The feeler of a beetle (enlarged 36 times). The efficiency of insects'
antennae as an olfactory organ is often astounding: many male butterflies scent the females from great distance with the aid of a fine
sense of smell localized in the antennae. Other insects can pass on
information by mutual contact with their feelers.

The eye of a fly.

The sinister effect of the cayman's glance is caused by the slitted pupils.

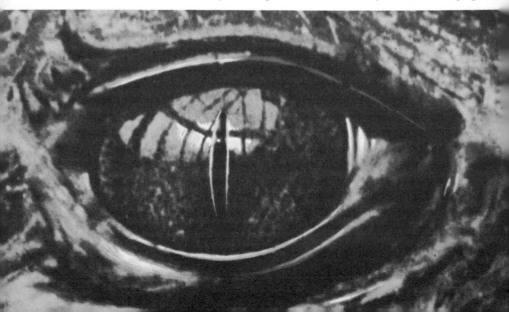

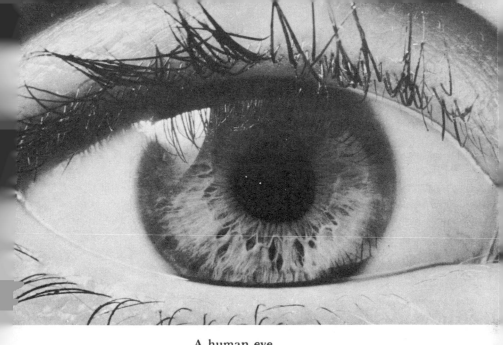

A human eye.

The eye of a bee.

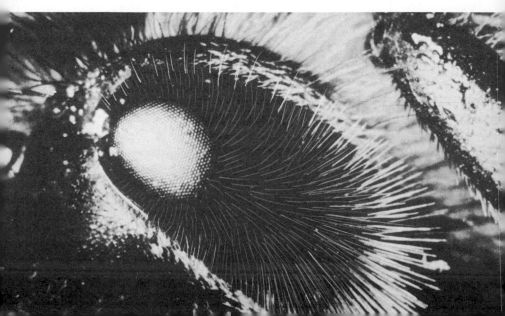

The bat finds its direction even on the darkest night with the help of a kind of radar apparatus.

we experience very bad pain inside the body. These are warning signals, bringing to our notice the fact that some danger is present, and nowhere is the alarm signal so effective as in the envelope of the body, the skin. Without the warnings from the tiny alarm stations registering "heat", "cold" and "pain" our lives would be in constant jeopardy. There is a certain disease called syringomyelia in which these three cutaneous senses no longer function properly. Victims of it usually exhibit bad burns or cuts about the body because they react too late when touching hot or sharp objects.

The cutaneous sense of touch is localised in the unevenly distributed pressure points, of which there are on an average 30 per sq. cm. of skin. Moreover, we find all manner of variations in the animal world and in certain plants, such as the ultra-sensitive mimosa. Even the lowest forms of life react to the irritations of touch, which warn them of danger and give them their bearings in space. Hairs or bristles are frequently used as additional sensitive organs for the reception of nervous stimuli—we only have to think of the long whiskers of a cat. Here life uses the leverage principle, for the pressure on the long bristles or hairs, transferred to the receptors, irritates them earlier, or more strongly, than would have been the case without this apparatus. Closely bound up with the sense of touch is the sense of equilibrium, which in vertebrates is located in the labyrinth of the inner ear. Here three semi-circular canals are so arranged that each of their planes is practically at right angles to the other two.

Special cells lying in the sack-shaped extensions of each canal regulate the sense of balance in two ways: first, the weight of the calcium excretions they contain presses downwards and indicates the position of the body in space; secondly, these sensory cells are irritated by the movements of the labyrinth liquid, or endolymph. Hence our fine sense for turning in space. Each of these twofold stimuli, transmitted to the vestibular nerve and the cerebellum, leads automatically to compensating movements—the so-called postural reflexes. When we stumble over a stone and change the inclination of the body, its sense of equilibrium quite involuntarily impels it to reassume its normal posture. If we try to make such movements voluntarily, we only disturb the course of events. Incidentally postural reflexes develop comparatively late. The baby flounders about like a sack of flour.

In the animal kingdom we find the prototype of the three canals of the labyrinth widely distributed as small ciliated vesicles. Upon these lie small bodies which, as in the case of our own balance organ, press downwards in accordance with gravity. On a change of position of the body in space, the sensory cells at the base of the vesicles are irritated and cause the animal to perform movements which bring it back to a normal posture. In the case of some animals these static organs are situated in the head and in others in the tail. The shrimp carries them in a cleft in its feelers, and each time this small crustacean sheds its carapace it has to use its pincers to fill the cavity with grains of sand, which serve as ballast. If iron filings are placed in the aquarium instead of sand it has to be content with these, and instructive experiments can be made. When a strong magnet is placed near the shrimp the iron filings irritate the sensory cells in the direction of the magnetic pull, and it is precisely in this direction that the shrimp turns its belly—so that the force of gravity remains "below". The pressure sense units are of extraordinary importance in all living creatures. They make possible, for example, the "current sense" of fish, which enables trout always to place themselves with their noses upstream.

As opposed to common belief, fish can also hear, although their hearing organ is comparatively simply built, lacking principally the cochlea of the inner ear; but, in spite of this deficiency, fish can be trained to obey certain feeding signals. They can certainly distinguish at least one octave, and this is sufficient, for in the life of these creatures fine differences in tone hardly matter. Recently dwarf sheat fish have been brought to react to certain calls. A male fish, Adam, and a female, Eve, would come out of their hiding places when their names were called. The reception and relaying of sound waves takes place with the aid of the air bladder connected to the inner ear by three small jointed bones.

It is easy to see how, in the course of evolution, the hearing organ of the land vertebrates developed from the simple hearing apparatus of the fish, one more proof that their forefathers and ours once lived in the sea. Briefly this transformation from a primitive to a brilliantly efficient hearing organ took place in the following manner. The air bladder and branchial clefts were abandoned as superfluous, and the hearing apparatus developed from the foremost branchial cleft; further refinements were then developed to improve the hearing organ, until finally Nature equipped the mammals—and only the mammals —with auricles. It is interesting to note that these "shells" were discarded by mammals when they returned to the sea. This applies to the whale, the dolphin and the seal. Nor has the mole any use for auricles and they were surrendered when he finally chose to live underground. Nature sees to it that all her creations are equipped to suit their needs. . . .

Many insects as well as vertebrates are able to hear. The organs, of primitive construction but nevertheless astonishingly versatile, are to be found in various parts of the anatomy—on the legs, the thorax or the abdomen—but these insect "ears" are really only a development of the static organs. Covering the sensory cells is a thin membrane, which originated from an extension of a trachea, and when it is set in motion by sound waves the vibrations are conducted to the sensitive cells. Their achievements are quite satisfactory, and the insects have no trouble in hearing tones which are naturally too high in the scale for our ears. Understanding by means of sound, with the aid of such ears on the legs or abdomen, is to be found in countless insects such as beetles, lice and butterflies. In the vertebrates the hearing organs are further developed, and in the mammals—and even in man, who is surpassed by a great many animals in this respect—they achieve astonishing efficiency. We may have learned in school how our ear is fashioned. It consists of an outer ear, with an auricle and ear-drum, the middle ear, and the inner ear or labyrinth, where the receptors for hearing and the sense of equilibrium unite. The sound receptor lies in the lower part of the labyrinth and looks like a snail shell—hence its name, the cochlea.

The sound waves are led through the auricle and the external auditory canal to the ear-drum, a membrane that lies between the canal and the middle ear. In mammals the sound vibrations are transmitted via three small movable bones, the hammer, the anvil and the stirrup, which are attached to a second membrane. It lies at the entrance to the inner ear and takes over the vibrations received from the ear-drum. Now the endolymph in the labyrinth accepts the vibrations and passes them on to the third and last membrane in the cochlea. This basilar membrane is the most sensitive of all and is a little masterpiece. It has long and short fibres running across it like the strings of a harp. Low tones cause the long fibres, and high tones the short fibres, to vibrate and irritate certain sensory cells in the cochlea, which transmit the irritation by way of the nerves to the brain. This is also the seat of the actual auditory impressions as they come to us in detail, and it perhaps explains why we find a Mozart Symphony beautiful and traffic noises appalling. Modern science can tell us very little about this factor in spite of a great many theories. We can distinguish variations in pitch ranging between 20 vibrations per second as the lowest tones and 20,000 per second in the upper range; very low and very high tones are not audible to us. Sensitivity to high tones decreases considerably during the course of our lives. A child can easily hear tones of 20,000 Hertz (1 Hertz = 1 vibration per second). Towards the end of puberty the upper hearing range has fallen by about 1,000 Hertz, and by the age of 35 by 5,000 Hertz. On average, a man of fifty will hear only tones up to 13,000 Hertz, and a very old man will barely hear 6,000 vibrations per second. The latter can no longer hear the notes of the cricket in the summer meadows.

THE "HEARING APPARATUS" OF THE BAT

As early as the eighteenth century the Italian naturalist Spallanzani tried to solve the riddle of the way in which bats find their bearings during their nocturnal flights. He strung a network of wires across his attic roof, where many bats lived, and noticed that they always avoided these obstacles. There-upon he caught a number of them and glued up their eyes, but their sense of direction was not in the least impaired. When he stopped up their ears, however, he found that they then flew into the wires. This simple experiment of many years ago proved that bats "see" with their ears, if we may be allowed the expression; but the principle involved was only discovered about twenty years ago, when, for the first time, some of the astonishing achievements of these flying mammals were finally explained.

During the Second World War the German biologist Professor Möhres and the American physicists Griffin and Galambos discovered independently that bats transmit tones of 30,000 to 80,000 vibrations per second, thus far exceeding the reception boundary of the human ear. These supersonic waves are reflected by resistant objects and are picked up by the ears of the bat in much the same way as our eyes pick up the reflected light vibrations from some object. If men and birds can be termed "seeing" animals, then bats should be termed "hearing" animals. With the aid of the supersonic waves they obtain a very precise spatial impression of their environment and have, for countless æons, used the principle which modern technology first used in the construction of echo-sounding equipment.

Research into this strangest of all hearing apparatuses devised by Nature for her creatures was an interesting and difficult task. It proved to be the case that the direction-finding organs of bats work in several different ways. The most common method used is orientation by tones produced by the mouth. If the animals have this source of sound-waves hampered by a kind of paper gag, their sense of navigation no longer functions.

Professor Möhres now demonstrated that bats of the species known as horseshoe-noses kept their mouths shut as they flew. The sounds serving for navigation were produced in the larynx and radiated via the nasal area. The so-called echoes, the sound-waves reflected from some obstacle, were picked up by both ears—in other words, by two separate "receiving stations" —thus increasing the accuracy of the bearing. The horseshoe-noses, as countless experiments showed, could avoid wires with a diameter of 1/10th mm. in complete darkness.

Even more remarkable are the feats performed by the Egyptian bat, which has two supersonic transmitters, one for general bearings and a second for precision direction-finding. The first note has a frequency of 120,000 Hertz—the absolute record for the highest "sound" emitted by an animal—while the second note, usually referred to as a call signal, has a frequency of 40,000 Hertz and serves, apparently, to pinpoint in space objects of special interest. As though this were not surprising enough, further research into the peculiarities of bats provides us with one more cause to marvel at the versatility of Nature in this field. It was found that in caves, cellars and other quarters where bats congregate the fliers never collide with each other in the dark. If they were all to send the same signal, two bats flying in close proximity towards an obstacle would receive each other's "echo" and be disturbed in their direction-finding. This obviously does not happen. Each bat therefore possesses its own personal transmitter, whose signals can be distinguished and recognised by other bats of the same species. As Professor Möhres recently reported in a lecture, there are about 1,000 different species of bats which fly both by day and by night. They can find their bearings optically or acoustically. In daylight they use their very efficient eyes and at nightfall switch over to supersonic transmission and use the acoustic method.

THE BLIND CAN "SEE" WITH THE EARS

It is now possible for human beings to "see" with their ears—that is to say, to find their way by hearing instead of sight. As opposed to the supersonic waves of the bats, invisible rays are used. In the USA a portable apparatus, working on the principle of radar, has been developed and has proved a very effective aid to the blind. The blind person carries in his hand a small case containing the equipment, which transmits a constant stream of electronic rays and is therefore known as the "electronic eye". The returning "echoes" are converted into tones. If the passage ahead is free of obstacles, the blind man hears a continuous normal tone in his ear-piece, or speaker, as the case may be. However, if a lamp standard, a wall or a door are in the way, the tone changes in an easily recognisable manner. After a little training a blind man can recognise any obstacle within a radius of 10 feet with the aid of the "electronic eye" and his ears.

Another apparatus for the same purpose works with photoelectric cells. The incoming light is transformed into electricity, which in turn produces tones. The most modern type consists of a metal rod weighing about 3 ozs., its most important component being an extremely efficient electric cell. As in the case of the apparatus just described, it is connected by means of wires to an ear-piece inserted in the blind man's ear. He probes the neighbourhood with his metal rod, and his ear receives the variations of brightness in the form of tone variations. Blind people usually possess a very acute sense of hearing and with a little practice it is not difficult for them to "hear" where the windows of a room or the various pieces of furniture happen to be. In relevant experiments with blind people all the furnishings of a room have been accurately recorded, and when led to a table laid for a meal they have been able to locate even the plates and cups after only a short test.

Admittedly this is only a beginning. We have today the possibility of making our environment acoustically visible, and Professor Möhres, at the end of a lecture on the direction-findings of bats, pointed out the possibility of adopting these methods for human beings and, in particular, for the blind. It is interesting to note that we can learn something not only from the behaviour but from the technique of animals.

THE "CHEMICAL" SENSES: SMELL AND TASTE

Earlier ages saw in man the most perfect of all creations, unsurpassed in all matters of sensory and intellectual achievement, but in these pages we have seen, more than once, that scientific findings give us ground in many respects to be more modest and to be wary of overestimating our capacity for knowledge or physical prowess. This applies particularly to the senses of smell and taste, by means of which chemical substances can be recognised in gaseous or dissolved states. In animals such sense organs, in all their possible forms, play a very important part, for they help them to find and select their food. Furthermore, the sense of smell is the "marriage broker" *par excellence* for many species, for it brings the sexes together. In mammals the nose is usually more important than the eye, and the power of dogs or deer to scent is far superior to the rather clumsy achievements of men.

Even the invertebrates, especially insects, perform miracles in this respect. We have only to recall the ichneumon wasp, which can smell out the position of a woodworm under the bark of a healthy tree. A certain species of fly lays its eggs only in truffles which grow below ground, and it can tell their whereabouts with unfailing accuracy. Butterflies recognise the small amounts of perfume emitted by the females over distances so great that it is hard to credit such a performance on the part of sensory organs. Recent experiments have shown that in many cases it needs only a few molecules of the perfume —an incredible dilution—to be present in the air for them still to be picked up accurately.

It is interesting to recall a famous experiment carried out by the French entomologist, Fabre. For years he had searched his region unsuccessfully for an emperor moth, which is found in those parts. He acquired a single caterpillar, and from the chrysalis eventually emerged a female moth. Fabre placed it under wire netting in his room, six feet from an open window, and within three days more than sixty males of this rare moth found their way there. It proved quite conclusively that the sense of smell was the guiding factor and that the insects' eyes played no part. After a time Fabre placed the female under a glass bell in the window and carried the sand on which she had sat to one corner of the room, with the result that all the males flew past the moth into that particular corner.

The olfactory organs in insects, as in crustaceans, are usually situated in the feelers. Ants whose feelers have been cut off, for example, can no longer distinguish members of an alien colony whom they usually recognise from their nest smell and proceed to kill. By the same token, a foreign ant which has been smeared with the body juices of ants from another nest is immediately accepted. Countless sensory cells are present on the feelers (in the male cockchafer there are about 50,000 and in the female about 8,000), which are susceptible to olfactory irritability. Since these antennæ are constantly in motion, as one can observe from any ant, insects are certainly better able than we to judge the distance of the source of an odour. Thanks to the spatial mobility of their antennæ, they can probably assess the shape of a body. If men possessed such organs, according to the observation of a certain well-known zoologist, "we should not only see that an apple is round but we could smell with closed eyes that it must be spherical".

Scents play another important part in the insect world, for it is known that bumblebees and wasps mark the path to the nest with certain odours, indications that are comprehensible to all the inhabitants of the nest. On analysis by chemical isolation, the "alarm material" used by the leaf-cutting ants has been found to contain a substance called citral. It is produced by the sentries of the colony in order to alarm the defenders when danger arises. Certain experiments carried out in Professor Butenandt's Institute gave rise to a rather surprising discovery of the effect of this substance on the ants. If too much citral were used, the alerted ants became so wild that they attacked each other.

As opposed to many fish and certain salamanders, whose sense of smell is more acute than ours, we can smell only gases. This would be of very little use in the water, for fish distinguish solutions—often very well—by their smell. Thus sharks make typical hunger movements if a hand which has touched a sardine is dipped only for a brief moment in the aquarium. A man, however, can fill his nostrils with the most expensive rose water and smell nothing at all.

In the case of mammals the sense of smell is located in the upper part of the mucous membrane of the nostrils. Countless sensory cells are irritated by gaseous materials inhaled, and this irritation is conveyed by way of the adjoining nerve fibres to the olfactory centre in the brain. Here the sensation of smell takes place. That is all we can safely say of its origin. As in the sensations of seeing and hearing, there are a great many theories current but none of them has as yet been proved. On the other hand, we know from intensive research that even men can work wonders with their sense of smell.

It has been found that we can distinguish about 10,000 different odours. A wealth of natural and artificial aromatic material has been tested to ascertain the minimum degree of dilution that can be detected. One five-millionth of a milligramme of vanilla per litre of air, an incredibly small amount of the substance, is enough to stimulate the mucous membranes. It must be recognised that most mammals can smell even lesser quantities, for their nostrils are equipped with far larger olfactory areas than are man's. Compared with them man has a pathetic nose, for once he rose up on to his hind legs soil odours played no further vital part in his life. For the same reason the tree-dwelling apes and birds generally have a very poor sense of smell.

Many other animals must be able to distinguish with their sense of smell not only sources of food but also their enemies and friends, and particularly members of their own species. To make the last task easier some of them possess special glands which secrete odoriferous substances. We have only to recall the scent glands which the deer carries between its hooves, the rutting gland of the chamois (it lies behind the crutch), or the well-known glands of the musk rat and musk ox. In certain cases such glands serve for defence, as with the skunk. From a distance of several yards, the skunk will squirt a fetid secretion from its glands which will cling to an enemy for months—an effective defence weapon that makes the skunk safe from practically any enemy.

APPLE OR POTATO?

Why not try out the following experiment one day? Close your eyes, hold your nose and bite alternately into an apple and a raw potato; or you can perform the same experiment with an onion and a strawberry. It will always be found uncommonly difficult, and often impossible, to distinguish these foodstuffs, which taste so very different, one from the other. The reason is that both the chemical senses, taste and smell, are closely associated. Admittedly the so-called "taste buds" of the tongue, which convey the irritations of taste to the brain, react only to dissolved materials, but, as every connoisseur of wine knows, smell also plays its part in sensations of taste. Moreover, the "appreciation" of the various taste qualities (sweet, sour, bitter and salty) depends upon the distribution of buds over various areas of the tongue: bitter is best experienced at the back of the tongue, sweet at its tip. When we have a cold everything seems tasteless. The nose is closed up and the smelling sensitivity of the mucous membranes fails because the gaseous matter cannot penetrate the olfactory cells.

In animals taste plays a far lesser role than smell. Many of them have their taste organs in their feet instead of in the normal place, the region of the mouth, and this is a very practical arrangement in the case of butterflies, which obtain their sugar-containing foods by means of a long proboscis. Were the taste organ to be located in the mouth, on testing each liquid it would have to fill the proboscis in order to determine whether the nectar were palatable. Nature has endowed these insects with very sensitive taste organs on their feet, which they do not have to use for dusty wanderings like other animals; thus there is no risk of the organ becoming clogged. It is probable that they rarely mistake a suitable food source. Taste organs of this type have been found in a host of butterflies, including the common cabbage white, and in many flies. Research shows that the highly sensitive feet of a fly react 300 times more accurately to a sugar solution than does the human tongue. In fact, flies can detect sugar when 1/100th of a gramme is dissolved in 17 pints of water. Examination has shown that the two forelegs of the fly possess the best "tongues", a practical measure because the insect approaches its food with them. Since smell and taste, in addition to their ordinary functions, are very important "control posts" for both man and animal, they are usually located in front, at the entrance to the body. Above all, a sensitive nose warns its owner of noxious elements in food or in the air, and in our case too, although we lag behind many of the mammals, it is a magnificent watchman in the service of our health.

A further sense which we must mention is the muscle sense, which registers the position of a muscle in relation to its environment. It is incorporated in a psychological unit with the senses of sight and touch. Then there are a number of special sensations, such as hunger and thirst, the feeling of well-being, and the urges to micturate and defecate. They derive to a great extent from very intricate combinations of different physical processes and call forth the well-known reflexes and sensations.

There is also a chemical sensory organ in the intestine, activated by acids, which plays a part in the regulation of the digestive movements. We realise its activity no more than we notice the fact that in every visual experience not only the eye as such, but also the muscle sense, plays a part by moving the relevant muscle. The visual impressions of the retina and the "reports" of the respective positions of the eye muscles are picked up in combination by the brain and transformed without our noticing anything of it. In animals there are presumably other sensory organs of a completely unknown nature. To quote but one example, the gnat must have a certain sense which gives it accurate information regarding the moisture content of the air. Certain animals and some men also have a very mysterious sense of orientation which enables them to find certain directions or landmarks without the aid of a compass.

The vast field of sensory perception is so complex and varied that further research into its problems may bring us many surprises.

CONTROL STATIONS IN THE BODY

Attention has been called to the fact that in the regulation of countless physical functions special "messengers", the hormones, play a major part. But even the incredibly precise interplay of the secretions of the endocrine glands would never suffice to guarantee the essential unity of the cell state. "Control stations" to rule all the organs are necessary, and the higher animals have this vital apparatus in the brain. In the case of protozoa it is unnecessary, for in these tiny aggregates of protoplasm all the life processes take place without stomach, intestine, heart or veins, and naturally also without a brain— and yet even these most primitive forms have the rudiments of the subsequent "control station". There are certain structures in the cell which respond to external irritation and give the organism, as in the case of the paramecium or slipper animalcule, a certain opportunity of learning by experience.

This was apparently shown by experiment. A large number of paramecia were placed in a drop of water, half of which lay in the light and half in the shade. At first it was a matter of indifference to the infusoria. They distributed themselves evenly throughout the whole drop. But as soon as the bright part grew warm they became uncomfortable and fled into the shady half, where they remained even after the whole drop had been brought back to an even temperature. As soon as they came to the light barrier they turned about rapidly although it was no warmer there than in the dark spot. Doubtless they had "remembered" that the light part had been unpleasantly warm. In a second experiment with new subjects, each was given a slight electric shock as soon as it reached the bright part of the drop. It resulted in all the paramecia turning about at the frontier between dark and light even when they received no shock. Naturally their memory was very short-lived. After about twenty minutes they had already forgotten what they had learned from the experiment; nevertheless it was a remarkable achievement for a unicellular creature.

In the metazoa we find in a rising line at all times a more complex tendency towards "control stations", with closely-linked conduits to receive the stimuli and pass on the information to the "control station". The small freshwater polyps have no brain but a network of nerves through which irritations can be led through the entire body. Of course, such an apparatus works very slowly, for in certain circumstances the stimuli to the nerves have to travel a very roundabout way and affect large regions of the body with which the particular irritation has nothing to do. In certain lower animals, such as the annelid worms, we find "relay stations" (ganglia) in each segment of the body. In these are united a host of nerve cells which are interconnected and are also linked with the sensory organs in the worm's head.

With the vertebrates this development leads to the creation of ever more efficient "control stations" in the body, the peak naturally being the human brain. Vertebrates possess a central nervous system which uniformly regulates all the physical processes; each irritation is led via the sensory nerves to the centre and is there transformed. The "orders" to reply to the stimulus are then given to the respective organs through the motor nerves. Among the ranks of the vertebrates we can clearly observe the tendency to further development of the cerebrum.

In the lower vertebrates the "compartments" of the brain, which originated from the fore-end of the spinal cord, differ comparatively little from each other in size. The higher we climb the evolutionary ladder of the vertebrates the more significant becomes the cerebrum, until in the mammals, and in particular man, it begins to play the dominating role within the hierarchy of the central nervous system. In the amphibians the cerebrum is still only in direct contact with the interbrain (diencephalon), but in the mammals it has become an entirely superior organ which controls—one might say in the manner of a supervisor—nearly all the physical processes. Moreover in man, as a centre of thought, it is the seat of consciousness as well as of all intellectual and spiritual processes.

MEMORY IS LIKE A SOUND FILM

Until recently modern man's knowledge of himself showed one particular lacuna: practically nothing was known of how our brain manages to preserve and, when necessary, to reproduce past memories and experiences. A Canadian scientist, Professor W. Penfield, Director of the Institute for Brain Research in Montreal, was able in part to solve this problem.

It is well known that in certain brain diseases or cases of concussion people "lose their memory". They forget their names, where they live, and in some advanced cases even forget how to light a cigarette or to open a door. Very old people may have difficulty in remembering the names of their grandchildren but can often recall with surprising accuracy events from their own youth.

There must therefore be certain imprints—they are known to scientists as engrams—which fix events, experiences, etc., in the brain. But how does this happen? In spite of intensive effort no hard and fast tracks of these memory-engrams could be traced until Professor Penfield discovered how Nature works in this respect. The memories are impressed electrically. It has long been realised that electric processes play an important role in physical events—for example, optical or acoustic impressions in the visual and hearing organs are transformed into infinitesimal electric charges and led through the nerves to the brain, where they evoke visual and auditory sensations. In the same way each thought process is associated with the production of certain electric waves. Something analagous occurs in the recording of the heart's activity, so that any cardiac patient can tell from the electrocardiogram whether the information recorded is good or bad.

In his search for the material bases of recollection of thoughts Professor Penfield subjected certain parts of the brain cortex to weak electric shocks. When he applied the electrodes to the region of the temporal lobes the "guinea pigs" immediately obtained certain precise memories of long-forgotten events. These memory pictures were at times so vivid that the perfectly normal subject mistook the present for the past during the experiment. Each time a certain spot on the temples of one woman was subjected to an electric shock she thought she heard a piece of music which had youthful associations she had long since forgotten. The auditory impression was so vivid that at first she was convinced that the music was being played on a gramophone in the next room.

In another case an elderly man thought he heard the laugh of a relative who had died many years before. Here, too, the same memory process was activated by stimulating a circumscribed zone of the temporal lobes. Our memory therefore, like seeing and hearing, depends upon electric processes in the brain. From his investigations Professor Penfield concluded that all the impressions of importance throughout our lives are electrically stored in certain zones of the brain and preserved like a kind of "sound film". What has once been learned can then be played back with all the optical and acoustic accompaniments provided the electrical "storage" was intensive enough.

The cerebrum never gives its information direct to the organs, since it has no connection with the nerves coming from outside, but always to the lower parts of the brain, i.e. the mesencephalon and diencephalon. Various physical processes are directed by these lower parts of the brain to the spinal cord or the autonomous nerve system, which is the centre for the involuntary physical functions such as glandular activities, etc. In the cerebrum all these functions are represented and co-ordinated to the highest degree. The superior activity of the cerebrum makes it understandable that when this organ has been operatively removed from a dog the animal will go on living because the physical functions will continue to be directed from the lower centres. Even a man whose cerebrum has been occluded by disease can continue to live, at least for a certain time, in a purely vegetative state. The cerebrumless dog can stand and run, can respond to stimuli, but all this happens automatically—"unintelligently", if we may be allowed the expression. If such a dog is stroked by its master, it will growl angrily or try to bite him. The centre of its defence mechanism, the interbrain, is retained, whereas the memory of its association with its master has been lost along with the cerebrum.

THE POWER OF REFLEXES

Birds without a cerebrum can still fly and land as far as this is possible for a creature that is then virtually blind. Such experiments were an important proof that even in highly complicated flight movements it was a question of pure reflexes, which take place without the intervention of the consciousness centred in the cerebrum. When a boy learns to ride a bicycle he at first finds it very difficult, for the task occupies his whole attention. In other words, he needs his cerebrum. Once he has acquired the correct technique in this or any other sport, such as skiing or swimming, the consciousness is no longer normally switched on, for the physical process has been "learned" and is now automatic. When we are out cycling we can therefore converse with a companion, a feat which as every cyclist knows would have been impossible at the learner stage. Matters are very different in the case of the motorist. He learns to react to traffic incidents largely by reflex, a fact which makes his responsible task easier because the reflex actions do not have to travel by way of the cerebrum. In certain circumstances many fractions of a second can be saved.

The actual significance of reflexes can be summed up broadly as follows: they are an important protective measure given by Nature to the body, which is constantly menaced from "outside". With the aid of acquired reflexes we can react correctly to a certain extent by instinct and thus master a difficult situation such as the avoidance of a fall in skiing. After the incident we cannot accurately say what we "thought" about it. The safety measure of the body against the fall went into action automatically; it was regulated by the labyrinth of the inner ear and a certain part of the brain, releasing postural reflexes whose aim was a swift recovery of balance. Had we actually fallen, it would have taken place as practically as possible, quite without our conscious intervention. This is a very important biological safeguard against accidents, but it applies only within certain boundaries of natural movement. If a man is flung out of a car in a crash, the safety measure fails because he can no longer behave correctly by instinct. In traffic accidents many bad injuries result because the biological potential for protection has been exceeded.

When dealing with the postural reflexes influenced by the static organ we mentioned that there are countless processes in the body which function automatically without the participation of consciousness. Such reflexes play a great part in our lives and a far greater part in the lives of animals. A physiologist once made an amusing remark on the subject. If a man, on waking, had to explain how many reflexes came into play during his normal day for the activities of walking and standing, he would presumably never leave his bed. Reflexes occur in a host of forms. They can deal with single movements or a whole chain of progressive actions; glandular secretions are stimulated by reflexes; we cough, sneeze, yawn, and swallow all by reflex action. These are "innate" reactions peculiar to each species, and all its members will react to the same stimulus and in the same manner. If the organism is tired or sick, reflexes can slow down or (as in strychnine poisoning) increase abnormally. The well-known patellar reflex, for instance, is used by doctors to diagnose the state of the central nervous system. Such unconscious processes will often be activated by the spinal cord, while others are directed by the brain.

In addition to the "innate" or simple reflexes there are others known as acquired or "conditioned" reflexes. Let us recall Pavlov's metabolic experiments with dogs, by which he demonstrated both types. A quickening of the digestive system was automatically induced by holding out food to the animal. This chain reaction (secretion of stomach juices) occurs in the same manner in every dog and is an unconditioned reflex. But when the experimental animal learned to associate certain sounds with food and the stomach juices began to flow—for example, at the ringing of a bell—this was an acquired or conditioned reflex.

MIGRATORY ANIMALS

Animals and plants have countless facilities for coming to terms with unfavourable living conditions, and in the course of these pages we have already become acquainted with phenomena of adaptability of the most varied types. The roving animal has a very simple method of coping with an unsuitable environment—it merely flees from it. We can observe this every autumn when our migratory birds assemble in their hosts and set out for winter quarters more favourable as regards food and climate. Bird migration has been studied extensively in the past few decades; hundreds of thousands of migratory birds have been ringed, and field naturalists have been able to give an excellent picture of their rate of travel, their routes and winter quarters. Science, however, still wishes to know the answer to one question: how do the birds find their way to foreign lands and back again to their homelands?

The first part of this problem has been closely studied at the bird-watching station of Rossitten. The most important subjects chosen for research were storks, whose routes have long been common knowledge. Storks that breed in Eastern Europe travel south-eastwards via Israel to their African quarters, whereas their West German counterparts take the south-westerly route via Gibraltar. Young birds were taken from their nests in East Germany, ringed, and held back until all the other storks had left in the autumn. The prisoners were then brought to Western Germany and released. The burning question now was whether they would follow the course of their western kin via Gibraltar or whether they would fly via Israel like their parents and fellow fledglings. The answer was surprising. The birds flew in the same south-easterly direction they would have had to take from their homeland and in this way reached Italy. The experiment clearly showed that migration rests on an innate knowledge of the direction to be taken on their journey to winter quarters.

But this is only one aspect of the problem, for migratory birds return home in the spring. How do they find their way back? To discover the answer a number of breeding birds were caught and released at varying distances from their nests. It was observed once more that most of the birds immediately took off in the direction of their nests. Most of them arrived home, and distance seemed to play little part. Starlings and swallows were despatched from Germany to Sweden and England, and most of them returned. A wryneck was flown from Berlin to Salonika and returned to its nesting-box ten days later. It had therefore flown 100 miles a day in the exact direction of its home.

The German zoologist Rüppell carried out a number of interesting experiments to check the sense of direction of birds.

He took some starlings on a journey and, with the aid of a clockwork cage, spun them round in an attempt to disorientate them. On release, these victims of his game of "blind man's buff" showed not the slightest uncertainty and made straight for their home. Everything goes to show that birds, quite regardless of the outward journey, have a clear homing sense and will fly in the appropriate direction without detour. They have never learned this faculty, for the young will find their way back without the leadership of their parents, as is proved by the cuckoo. The parent cuckoos, which never rear their young, set forth on their own for Egypt and the Sudan. A little later they are followed by the youngsters, which have been brought up in other birds' nests, and they cover the long stretch with no difficulty. How reliable this sense of direction is has been proved in practice by a ringed cuckoo that has been watched for twelve years and has always reappeared in May at exactly the same place.

As regards flying distance, the magnificent achievements of the migratory birds can certainly compete with modern aircraft lines. The American golden plover crosses the Atlantic, and the Arctic tern undertakes a journey twice a year amounting each time to about 10,500 miles. The record in sense of direction is held by one of the shearwaters, which spends the summer in the English coastal areas but for some unknown reason eventually breeds on the little rocky island of Tristan da Cunha in the South Atlantic.

We find the same basic pattern evidenced by birds in the migration of fish. Salmon will often cover enormous distances in their travels to the spawning grounds up the rivers. The American king salmon makes a twice-yearly journey of about 1,800 miles and in addition has to negotiate all types of obstacle in the rivers. Eels reverse this procedure. They arrive on the European coasts as elvers in their fourth year of life and travel up rivers and brooks to their sources. There they remain for some years until they are fully mature, when they set out once more on their journey, this time downstream towards the sea. Until recent years there was a "riddle of the eels", for no one knew where they went on this second spawning journey. Finally they were traced, and today we know where they spawn—in the Sargasso Sea in the West Atlantic. Here they meet eels from the Baltic and the North Sea, eels from the Mediterranean and America, and all of them celebrate their marriage in the same waters. After spawning the old eels seem to die off very quickly, for a mature eel has never returned to the rivers from the ocean.

The migrations of birds and fish have been studied down to the smallest detail. We know the seasonal rhythms at which they occur and we know that hormonal control plays a part in their determination. But there is still a completely unsolved problem which has perplexed naturalists for a very long time: how do the migratory animals find their goal? As we have already said, the presence of a sense of direction was confirmed, after much experimentation, but how does it work? We might imagine that birds take their bearings from some landmark in the countryside and find their way by virtue of their "birdseye view" of the land below. This would not help them, however, in alien territory when the distances become too great—as, for example, in the experiments mentioned above, when birds such as swallows were despatched some 1,200 miles from their nests. They returned home, exactly as salmon return on their spawning journey to the spot in the river where they themselves emerged from the egg. Salmon could hardly notice any details of the river bank formation and there are no landmarks in the water itself. Fish of course have a sense of current, by which migrating eels also find their direction, but this will by no means explain the home-coming of the salmon. In the past few years the researches of the American hydrobiologist Hasler have brought a little progress. We know that fish have a very well-developed sense of smell and Hasler managed to prove that it was this sense that enabled them to distinguish between different types of water. Presumably, then, the salmon's home river has a specific nest smell which the fish remembers even after a sojourn of several years in the sea.

All manner of theories have been advanced in an attempt to solve these problems. Migratory birds have been credited with a sense organ that responds to changes in the earth's magnetic field, thus offering them a stage by stage return to the longitudes and latitudes of their home area. Recently this idea was confuted by a very simple experiment. In one of the despatching experiments magnets were attached to certain birds, or they were brought into a strong magnetic field just before release. This made not the least impression on them and they flew straight as a die for home with or without the magnet. American bird-watchers in light aircraft have followed the routes of gannets (*morus bassanus*) which had been taken from their nests and later released. For almost ten hours and over a stretch of several hundred miles the zoologists followed the flight of homing birds in their slow machine. The gannets were completely undisturbed by their noisy companion, for the percentage of "homecomers" remained the same as in all the other experiments. None of these flights has so far brought any solution. The late W. Rüppell, who ranked as an expert in this field, took the view in his later work that the most plausible answer to the conundrum is to be found in orientation by the relative position of the sun. There is something to be said for this if we consider the findings of von Frisch on the language of the bees, which inform fellow members of their hive of good sources of food by taking into account the position of the sun. Although these and other investigations in recent years lend support to the theory of solar orientation on the part of migratory birds the problem of how they find their way on their travels in the dark still remains.

In the past few years the researches of the zoologist Sauer have given rise to a brand new theory. He demonstrated the fantastic fact—or at least made it seem plausible—that by night birds take their bearings from the stars. The take-off of birds released in a planetarium was noted, and the position of the stellar constellations proved to be of striking significance. For example, flycatchers from the north travel to Germany in a south-easterly direction. In the planetarium, when they were shown the night-sky above Turkey, they flew south, and so would duly have reached their African winter quarters. It is exciting to think where this new line of research may lead us in some years' time. In any case, it once more shows that the Ancient Egyptian astronomers, in their direction-finding by the stars, already had their forerunners in the birds they portrayed in their hieroglyphs.

Extraordinary feats of homing have been observed in mammals, particularly in dogs and cats. The well-known animal psychologist Bastian Schmid left dogs at varying distances from their homes and followed their behaviour. In one experiment a peasant dog was placed in a closed truck and taken to the prescribed starting point a long way from its home, the truck zig-zagging across hills and forest regions unknown to the dog. As soon as the animal was put down it tried to get its bearings with its *eyes*, and not its nose, and after some hesitation it trotted off in the direction of its village, where it arrived in due course safe and sound. In principle the same results were achieved with an urban dog which Schmid set down in a completely strange part of Munich. Despite the particular difficulties posed by city traffic and the uniform pattern of the streets this dog, after twenty-five minutes' pause to find its bearings, found the right way home. Many similar experiments made with dogs, cats and even mice have led to the conclusion that such animals possess a sense of direction of which we still know basically nothing.

On the other hand, we can at least hazard a guess why Nature endowed her creatures with such gifts. Were there no homing urge, there would be a danger of areas particularly favourable as regards climate or food attracting huge surpluses of animals, while less favourable regions would be denuded of their populations. Nature seems determined that, within the framework of possible adaptability, her creations should be distributed over the whole earth. Thus instinct compels migratory birds in the spring to leave the rich feeding-grounds of their winter quarters and to undertake the arduous, dangerous journey to their northern breeding grounds.

Conversely, the "wander lust" sometimes serves to decimate living creatures when, as the result of over-procreation, they threaten to disturb the ecological balance. The most famous example of this is afforded by the suicidal migrations of the lemmings. These little rodents live in the mountainous parts of Scandinavia, and the females normally have litters once or twice a year. In extremely fertile years the females can have as many as ten. The result is naturally an enormous over-population of lemmings, which leads to lack of food in their pastures and a compulsion to migrate in their hosts. When they reach the coast the animals cascade like a waterfall over the cliffs. Those that are not dashed to pieces on the rocks leap into the water and try to swim away from land until literally the last lemming is drowned. The same catastrophe occasionally overtakes grasshoppers and other insects when they embark upon mass migrations in search of new sources of food and in their fatal Odysseys happen to come to a coastal area.

ANIMALS HELP EACH OTHER

In the eternal battle that rages between pursuer and pursued it often happens that various individuals of both groups will join forces in attack or defence. Perforce hunting is a favourite trick used by carnivores in order to reach their prey more easily. Wolf packs in pursuit of game often split into two sections, one pursuing the fleeing game directly while the other tries to head it off. Our harmless house dogs have a certain recollection of these customs, for during the First World War the naturalist Alverdes was able to watch several genuine pack hunts by hungry dogs in areas abandoned by the inhabitants. A motley crew of ten or twelve dogs scoured the fields in search of hares or rabbits. While wintering on the African steppes white storks on the hunt for locusts at times even join forces with marabous. Pelicans fishing in shallow waters are known to help each other. They form a circle which grows ever narrower, driving the fish into the centre so that each bird can catch its own portion. Mutual aid is usually confined to hunting; when it comes to sharing the booty the communal rule ceases and the law of "might is right" prevails.

Like the hunters, the hunted frequently co-operate. We know, for example, that the warning cries of most of our native singing birds are very similar, but in general animals understand the warning notes of other species. In most cases help is unintentional and it is certainly so in the case of the frog. When a frog jumps into the water all the other frogs in the pond are alerted and are prepared to follow the example of their companion at the slightest disturbance. An amazing variety of warning signals is to be found among mammals: the marmot whistles, the wild rabbit drums on the ground with its hind feet, as does the kangaroo. . . . Many animals even post sentries during the night. Cranes and flamingoes use this device for protecting their flocks from attack. Some of our rooks each day take over the thankless task of sentry while the flock is foraging in a field. It sometimes happens that completely different animals help each other in this way. Zebras and gazelles will join up with ostriches to form a common herd, a precautionary measure of advantage to all parties. The ostrich has magnificent eyesight but hears and scents less keenly than the gazelle, so that the enemy whose presence is perhaps overlooked by one is noticed by the other.

The well-known motto "unity is strength" seems to have been adopted by small birds such as sparrows, which will usually give loud cries of alarm if, for instance, an owl is in the vicinity. These cries, heard on all sides by other small birds, bring them fluttering round the robber—only in daylight of course—who finds himself mobbed by a host of twittering birds which betrays his whereabouts to the world at large and spoils any chance he has of hunting. It is very rare that help is given to a wounded animal and only the higher species practise anything resembling care for the sick. Presumably the prerequisite for such behaviour entails a high mental capacity and a feeling of personal friendship between individuals.

Elephants and apes in particular help their wounded comrades. Big game hunters have often watched an elephant using its trunk to prod one of its shot companions to its feet again. Apes, as opposed to nearly every other animal, carry off their wounded and dead whenever possible. They also render little mutual services and will remove thorns and splinters from each other's fur after a hunt through the bush. Ants are believed to practise some sort of sick nursing; on the other hand, it has frequently been observed that they leave their sick or wounded unattended or carry them away to their refuse dumps.

The most touching forms of friendship and aid can be observed on occasions in chimpanzees, a fact which encouraged American zoologists to throw more light on the behaviour of the subjects. They put two chimpanzees in adjacent cages. One of them was given food, the other nothing. The deprived beast began to beg by stretching his hand through the bars to the other chimpanzee.

The success of the begging differed according to the character and mood of the owner. Sometimes he shared his food with his comrade or at least threw a few scraps into his cage. Often the plea was refused out of hand, a back was turned on the beggar, or he was even threatened. Nevertheless the inclination to give was quite strongly developed, for in the experiments out of 266 demands for charity there were 149 successes—more than half. Moreover, it often happened that the chimpanzee with the food freely gave of his bounty without waiting to be asked.

BUSINESS-LIKE ANIMALS AND PLANTS

The mutual aid of which we have just spoken usually develops from a given situation and is mostly of a transitory nature. There are, however, communities in Nature where the partners work together permanently, not of course out of idealism, which one cannot expect of animals, but to their mutual advantage. The classic example of this symbiosis, as it is called, is the landlord–tenant arrangement between the hermit crab and the sea anemone. These crabs have soft hind parts with no carapace and therefore occupy empty snail shells, which they carry around with them perpetually. The shells now become the favourite living-space of the most varied species of almost stationary sponges and sea anemones, which are carried about the food-laden sea bed by the crab and in addition profit by the scraps from the latter's meals. They pay well for their favourable dwelling for with their caustic stinging tentacles they defend their host successfully against countless enemies. The bodyguard is of no use to the crab when his weight increases and he is forced to give up his safe asylum and look for a new lodging. To save him this trouble many of the plumose anemones enlarge his living-space by expanding, so that finally the crab is to an extent enveloped by a protective living mantle. Even when the capacity of the anemone to grow is exhausted and the crab grows even larger the two remain together. Zoologists have often watched this common house-moving take place. The sea anemone, contrary to its usual practice of clinging fast at the slightest touch and putting out its stinging tentacles, voluntarily releases the crab from its base and allows itself to be transplanted to the new shell.

An almost unbelievable exploitation of such readiness to

help is to be found in small crabs that grasp a sea anemone in each claw and hold them out against enemies as defence weapons. The crab's claws are anatomically adapted for this purpose, possessing indentations which conform perfectly to the body of a certain sea anemone. In one special case the sea anemone appears as the landlord. In tropical seas a small fish lives permanently among the tentacles of the anemone, which never harms him. Here he feels secure from his enemies and displays his gratitude, as can often be observed in the aquarium, by catching scraps of floating meat and not only carrying them to the anemone but actually feeding them to it. He presses the food into the maw after biting off a little piece for himself. The protector gets the lion's share. This friendship is so close that the fish does not flee when the sea anemone is taken out of the sea, but goes into voluntary captivity. A similar instance is known in the North Sea. A shoal of young fish often swims among the tentacles of big jelly fish and find asylum under this umbrella. There can be no question of gratitude here for the young tenants from time to time nibble at their hostess.

Cases of true symbiosis are by no means rare in the plant world, where the idea seems to have originated with the lichens. Close study reveals that they are not single plants but an association of fungi and algæ. These two plants with completely different organisations complement each other in the most perfect manner. With the aid of its chlorophyll the alga is capable of assimilation and therefore takes its food, at least in part, from the oxygen in the air; the fungus, however, protects the alga from drought and is in a position to extract water vapour from moist air. Together algæ and fungi continue their modest existence on stones and trees as lichens, whereby each is dependent upon the other.

Scientists have been able to produce lichens artificially. Certain algæ and fungi, which normally have nothing to do with each other, were brought together experimentally, whereupon they joined as a lichen. A similar partnership contract, very important for human beings, is found in the leguminous plants. They work in close co-operation with certain bacteria that live in their roots, for these "tenants" are in a position to break down directly the nitrogen in the air, whereas the plants can only absorb it in the form of soluble salts. The rent is paid in nitrogen, which the bacteria deliver to the plants, and incidentally they first acquired this faculty in association with the higher plants. We find a similar symbiosis in many of the papilionaceous flowers, which in this way are able to thrive on nitrogen-poor soil. The importance of nitrogen–symbiosis in agriculture is displayed above all by lupins, which produce 438 lbs. of nitrogen per $2\frac{1}{2}$ acres—i.e. far more than is contained in 656 lbs. of horse manure. The working agreement between the partners in this "business" is so satisfactory that various strains of bacteria have developed for the various *papilionaceæ*. When, for example, the soya bean, so popular today, is planted in a new area the necessary soya bacteria must be added in the sowing or directly to the soil for the plant to thrive.

A further type of symbiosis is the relationship between the pollenising insect and the flower, which we have already discussed at length. The two partners virtually form a unit and they have been described as an "organism of the higher order". In actual fact flowers and insects are so ideally suited that many of them could not live without the other. There are countless cases of intimate collaboration between plants and animals which far exceed the basic principle of the plant as the primeval nourishment of all animal life. Possibly the most subtle business partnership between the two is to be found in the so-called ant-plant. This is a tropical growth which places at the disposal of certain harmless ants a particularly favourite abode in their tall stalks or thorns, and even goes so far as to provide them with foodstuffs containing glucose and protein. In return the lodgers help them against the dangerous leaf-cutting ants, which can sometimes devastate entire tropical forests. As soon as the robber ants approach, the protector ants rush out in their hosts and drive the enemy away. The plant is saved and the partnership has proved its worth. These are only a few of the examples of mutual aid in Nature, but they prove clearly enough that co-operation has its advantages even in the struggle for existence. For many living creatures this mutual support represents the prerequisite of their existence.

CHAPTER VII

The Span of Life

A PRETTY insect sits on a grass stalk and for the first time in its life airs its tender green wings. It has completed the cycle from larva to winged imago; soon it will celebrate marriage; and by nightfall it will be dead, having succumbed to old age. The ephemera seldom lives for more than one day. Nature has given other animals far more time to accomplish what this little creature has to cram into such a short time—into the course of its life as a mature insect. At the other end of the scale the record is undoubtedly held by the giant tortoise. A corroborated age of 120 years has been recorded in a specimen of *testudo Daudinii*, and it is probable that another of these reptiles is more than 200 years old. Only in the case of these giant tortoises—very indolent creatures that sleep half their lives away—can such great ages be recorded for certain; the figures given for other animals are usually false. The Indian elephant reaches a hundred years at the most and the whale, which is reputed to be longer-lived, never in actual fact reaches more than fifty. Carp may perhaps live eighty years, the sheat fish ninety, and the salmon a mere twenty to twenty-five. And what of the parrot? The figures so often quoted of parrots reaching a century or more are untrue, as recent research has shown. These birds rarely reach an age of fifty years and at the utmost sixty. Camels live to be forty, brown bears the same age, lions and tigers twenty to twenty-five, chimpanzees and orang-outangs not above thirty.

With the single exception of the Indian elephant among the vertebrates man alone, in exceptional cases, has a chance of passing the hundred year mark. But where is the maximal limit of human longevity? The question has usually been answered incorrectly, as modern research into old age has shown. Dr. Ernest of Great Britain came to the following conclusion after a lifetime of work in this field: "I must confess that there are very few human matters which have been more obscured through ignorance, falsehood and conscious roguery than the problem of longevity in man. This also applies to animals." We can understand Dr. Ernest's acid comment for in his country there are two star cases on record. Many authorities have insisted that the record is held by two Englishmen—Thomas Parr and Henry Jenkins, who were said to have reached the ages of 169 and 152 respectively. However, by consulting reliable documents, Dr. Ernest was able to establish the true ages of Parr and Jenkins. It appears that both men died long before reaching a hundred, but that they had given false details of their age and gained a great deal of money by so doing.

Men naturally want to live to grow as old as possible, and it was perhaps encouraging for the contemporaries of the celebrated Zaro Agha to realise that he was still active enough to travel about the world at the age of 150—and incidentally to take a great deal of gate money in return for allowing himself to be admired. But his reported age was as false as in other similar cases. Another source of error is due to unreliable official records. Bulgaria is notorious in this respect and might almost be called the Eldorado of old people. A census taken in 1926 showed that some 1,800 Bulgarians had reached the age of a hundred and more. Government officials were sceptical. They caused enquiries to be made, with the result that most of the old people admitted that they had no idea when they were born, but had merely estimated their age. By checking the parish registers and other records it was found that in Bulgaria at the time of the census there were only 51 people who had reached the age of a hundred and over. Today all experts agree that the limit of the human lifespan lies between 110 and 120 at the outside. At the time of writing the oldest man in the world is a Canadian shoemaker named Joubert. He has reached the age of 113.

ARE THERE IMMORTAL LIVING CREATURES?

The absolute age record among all the inhabitants of the earth is held neither by a man nor an animal, but by a plant— the Californian Sequoia. By counting the annual rings and by using other methods of checking some of the trees have proved to be more than 4,000 years old. Yews, cedars, and plane trees can live to be more than 1,000, but even such giants finally age and die, so it would appear to be an inalienable law of Nature that all living creatures must grow old and eventually die. But is this true?

We know that cells taken from a chicken or some other living creature can be preserved in alimentary liquid indefinitely. From this it would seem that death is not an unconditional function of life—in any case, not death in the normal sense of the word, i.e. the leaving behind of a dead organism. The same applies to unicellular creatures such as the amœba. When well-nourished the latter grows rather quickly (in a few hours) to double its original size. It is now fully grown and divides in accordance with its uncomplicated method of reproduction. A protozoon of this type undergoes binary fission, which means one living creature becoming two, the same performance being repeated a little later. Admittedly in a very high percentage the protozoa die, but they die an "unnatural" death from external circumstances. They have been termed "potentially immortal", and this theme has been a favourite topic for discussion among biologists for the last few decades. Today the question can be considered solved, but in the negative sense. There is no such thing as immortality from a biological standpoint.

This can be proved experimentally with protozoa. If in the relevant artificial conditions (concentrated alimentary liquid) division is prevented, they grow to many times their normal size. By so doing they lose their "immortality", for these single-celled creatures age and die exactly like any other living creature. From this we can draw the conclusion that no individual is really immortal, whether it be a member of the protozoa or the metazoa. In the first case the material available is used for the building of two new individuals at division; in the case of the multicellular animals it goes into general circulation after death. Individual survival is undoubtedly not in Nature's plan. This is quite understandable, for otherwise the earth would be so full of organisms that there would be no room at all for their issue. The spark of life is thus passed on in an endless chain of generations and as such remains immortal, whereas the individuals have only a limited span of life according to their nature.

TO AGE IS OUR FATE

Weismann, the great Freiburg zoologist, pointed out that the "discovery" of individual ageing, and with it physiological death, was probably made at a definite point in the history of life on this planet. At some place and time the original uni-cellular organisms must have formed into colonies—into com-munities, as it were—in which various groups of individuals were occupied in different activities. Such structures exist even today in the most varied forms, and they are very interesting subjects for the study of the process of ageing.

Let us take as our example a colony of *volvox globator*, one of the diatoms. The colonies consist of about 10,000 individuals, each of which possess as a nucleus, a cytoplasm, and flagella for locomotion. The members of the colony are united by a gelat-inous envelope from which the flagella protrude. One part of the member cells behaves like all unicellular creatures, and these are the procreators. They see to it that by fission or the formation of sexual cells new daughter colonies will be born. The number of these procreative individuals is relatively small, and after a certain time all the other members of the volvox colony age and die.

We are only too familiar with the external phenomena in the ageing of multicellular creatures. Men and animals at an advanced age show particular signs: the skin becomes wrinkled and flaccid, the organs (above all the sense organs) fail more and more in their capacity, the hair recedes, and the muscles turn to fat. The signs of old age in the lower animals have been recognised in part during research. For example, with age the tiny radiolarians show typical structural changes in the body and their movements slow down. The chitin carapace in ageing insects becomes brittle, antennæ and legs break off, and the intestine degenerates. When we eat the meat of old animals we find in its toughness another factor in the ageing of higher life—the increase of connective tissue in the muscle substance. In certain types of cell, age can be observed by very typical symptoms. Thus the nerve cells of a very old animal differ considerably from those of young animals. In the former we find deposits of dark pigment granules, and the neurons of old dogs show the same signs of advanced degeneration that occur in a corresponding form in birds and bees. In animals and men, therefore, the nervous system shows a particularly radical and incidentally comparatively early onset of the ravages of age. Many biologists have tried to trace the process of age back to the nervous system and its influence on the whole organism, but certain facts gainsay such a theory—*inter alia* the fact that it is not always the nerve cells that begin to age first: other equally vital body cells are often used up before them.

THEORIES OF AGE

Ever since man started to think about himself he has been preoccupied with the question of growing old. With the rise of natural science and its ever-increasing specialisation, the problem has been studied from various angles. Biologists and doctors, physiologists and pathologists, have sought to elucidate the processes involved with exact methods and to discover their actual cause, not to mention the efforts of the natural philosophers who, for their part, have added a host of theories. The oldest, and for the layman most plausible, explanation is the so-called theory of "wear and tear". It sounds quite acceptable because all the known signs of age in men and animals closely resemble those processes we can observe in an old car or a worn-out machine.

But this breakdown theory has recently been contested with so many cogent arguments that it can no longer be considered to apply, at any rate in its original form. The fact that in the bodies of multicellular animals the living substance is subject to constant metabolism and renewal speaks decisively against the idea of "wear and tear". Furthermore, the Leipzig physician M. Bürger, the leading German specialist in this field, has proved by systematic experiments on the aorta of old horses that it is not simply a question of "exhaustion" in the ageing organ. Were this the case the aorta should become weaker in the course of a lifetime. In practice it is the reverse. In horses, and even in humans, the aortic walls do not grow thinner but stronger. It is a question, according to Bürger, not of "wearing out" but of the rebuilding of the ageing vascular wall. Presumably the strengthening of the aortic wall is a compensatory reaction for its decreasing elasticity with age.

A certain school attempts to explain old age by increasing

A snail's tongue, greatly enlarged.
The rasping surface is clearly shown.

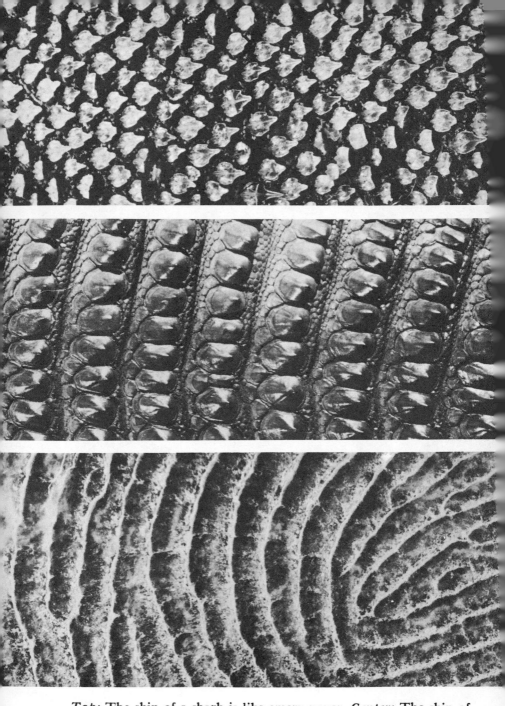

Top: The skin of a shark is like emery paper. *Center:* The skin of an iguana. *Lower:* A human finger tip with its characteristic lines.

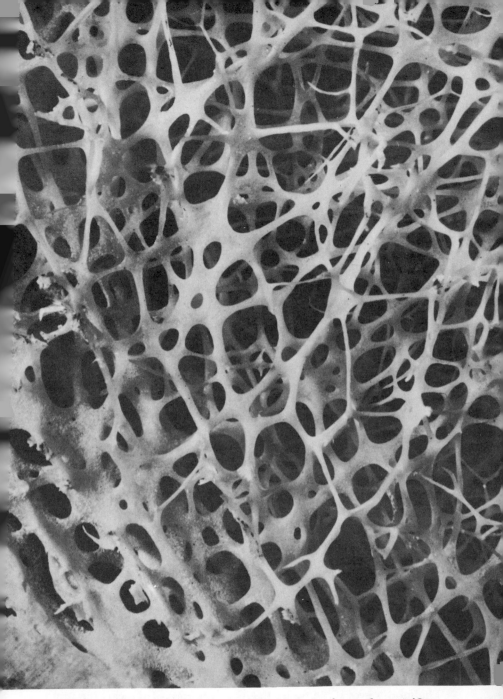

An interesting study of bone construction. It shows the ramifications of the spongy bone tissue, the so-called trabecula, in its transition to solid substance (enlarged 20 times).

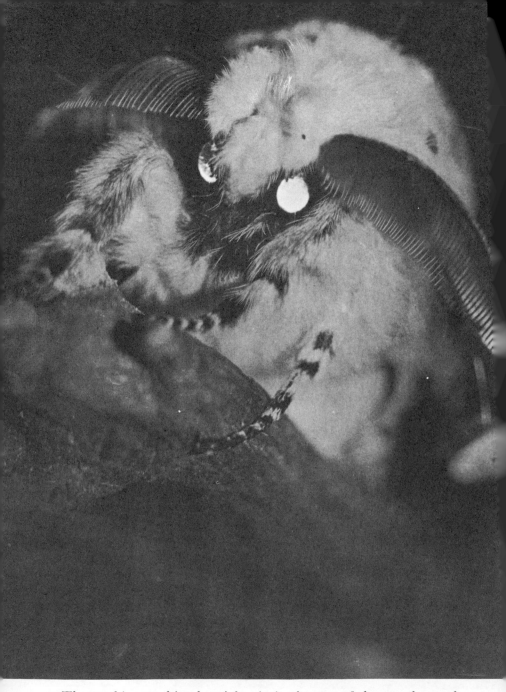

The moth's eyes shine by night. As in the case of the cat, the moth has a substance called guanin located on the retina. This reflects the slightest glimmer of light, causing the eyes to gleam.

poisoning or scorification of the body. According to this view, the cells poison themselves progressively in the course of a lifetime by their own metabolic products. According to Metschnikoff, the colon is the main culprit since, during the constant decaying processes, it forms toxins which ultimately damage the whole body. Other theories make cosmic radiation or the effects of radium emanations from the soil responsible. Proof is lacking in all these theories, and thus we shall confine ourselves to a brief mention of them. None actually explains the fact that neither the protozoa nor the germ plasm of multicellular animals becomes poisoned. As in many other theories, the premises—e.g. the observation of the presence of a growth-arresting material in the blood of very old people, for which there is much to be said—may be correct, but the interpretation placed upon them is wrong. Damage to cells and organs observed in ageing organisms is probably not the cause but the result of the process of ageing.

Today many leading scientists doubt whether we are entitled to attribute the ageing process to any particular factor. This doubt arises from two further theories as to the actual cause—firstly, the slackening of the hormone production of the endocrine glands, and secondly, a decline in the activity of the brain and the central nervous system. Steinach tried to make the enfeeblement of the sexual gland functioning responsible for old age. Lorand blamed the degeneration of the thyroid gland, and Raab the pituitary gland. But as regards the different endocrine glands whose degeneration has been put forward as a decisive cause we have only to point out the very revealing experiments of Bürger. By weight comparison he has shown that none of the above-mentioned glands can be considered as a *Deus ex machina*, for the average weight attained in old age by testicles, ovaries, thyroid and pituitary glands, shows no exceptional change in any of these glands. They all degenerate with age and, with the exception of the ovarium, which is subject to its own temporal norm, obey the "laws of ageing". This law consists in a progressive uniform degeneration with age, to which all the organs of our bodies are subject in varying degrees.

TO LIVE IS TO AGE

If, as so much evidence would lead us to assume, ageing—at least primarily—is not caused by "wear and tear", or poisoning and other damage to cells or individual organs during a lifetime, how is this phenomenon to be explained? The theories so far discussed approach the concept too narrowly, inasmuch as the gradual degenerative process during the period of life is considered as being "in the body". We come nearer to the crux of the matter if we cease to consider ageing as the breakdown of the "living machine", or something of that nature, but as the proto-phenomenon of life itself. Its manifestations cannot be explained mechanistically: we can only try to interpret them legitimately in the light of the whole process. Viewed from such a standpoint, the concepts "development of the individual" and "growing old" are on the same lines; in fact we must describe the phenomena of age in a narrower sense as development processes. There is no life without ageing, nor is there life without individual death, whether a corpse be left behind as in the case of the metazoa or whether the individual merely disappears by division as with single-celled living creatures. In principle there is no difference. In the case of the protozoa life continues through the melting of the individual structures and in the metazoa through the potentially immortal gametes or germ cells.

Ehrenberg, in summing up the findings of modern research into the problem of old age, came to the conclusion that ageing constitutes a process of form-impression and individualisation lasting the entire life span of the individual. The form, once laid down, undergoes constant change, which continues uninterruptedly from the beginning to the end. In the case of man this form-change takes place in spheres in accordance with his psycho–physical existence. Many organs and tissues are constantly transformed—for example, the skin, hair, and nails by excretion of some of the forming parts. In other cases, as with the blood corpuscles, the created forms are renewed after a certain period. On the other hand, there are organs which achieve their final impressed form, and with it their full function, only in the course of life. In this category belong the procreative organs and their co-operating hormone glands.

From this new viewpoint, which gains more and more adherents every day, ageing is no "basic constructional error" on the part of life, as the theories of "wear and tear", scorification in the organism or auto-intoxication of the cells, would have us believe. It is far more the self-realisation of the individual fettered to a beginning and an end. From the first phase of development of the fertilised ovum to the stage of great age runs a continuous line whose course is determined by the decline of the indeterminate, of the still possible, and by the progress of the realised.

WE LIVE EVER LONGER!

Will we ever see the day when most humans will live to be more than a hundred? This is, in fact, no Utopian thought, for biologists have long since maintained that man should reach a far greater age than is the general rule. The opinion is based on the fact that most living creatures reach six times the age represented by their maturation period. If growth is retarded artificially by providing the appropriate conditions, the duration of life can be extended considerably. At Cornell University M. McCay divided rats into two groups, one of which was fed normally and the other given a diet containing sufficient vitamins and minerals but too few calories. The oldest rat on the normal diet reached an age of 965 days, whereas the "undernourished" rats, after the same period, were still not fully mature and therefore were young and active. By prolonging the maturation period the appearance of old-age phenomena were substantially postponed.

A human being normally takes about twenty years to mature, hence his maximal span should be 120. This roughly corresponds with the existing method of working out the maximal age of a human being. We have already set the outside limit of 120.

Modern man has undoubtedly achieved much success in his efforts to prolong his span of life. According to statistics (discounting the risk of war), a baby born in Germany in 1870 had the prospect of reaching an age of 35. In 1900 the "average expectation of life" had already risen to 49, and a child born in a civilised land today has an expectation of more than 65 years. In former centuries the average lifespan was far lower, and in the pre-Christian era it has been found from a study of the memorials on tombs that most of the deaths occurred between the ages of 20 and 30.

This remarkable rise in the expectation of life is due to a variety of causes. In the first place it can be attributed to the success of modern medicine and hygiene, whereby a number of diseases previously considered incurable have been brought under control. Dangerous epidemics—we have only to recall the plague, cholera or smallpox—have virtually disappeared from civilised countries. Moreover, the infant mortality rate has been substantially lowered, and the mother's risk in child-birth compared with earlier ages has been greatly reduced.

The much-abused "modern" life is in many respects healthier than that of aborigines, whose environment does not encourage them to reach a very great age. Research among the most primitive races in all parts of the globe has shown time and time again that death from senility or advanced age is a rarity, and among these races the infant mortality rate is also extremely high. But even in Europe a few centuries ago it was not un-usual for more than 50% of newborn babies to die. Today in civilised countries the figures have been reduced to 30 to 40 deaths during the first year of life per 1,000 babies. As late as 1880 in Germany, on the other hand, 223 out of each 1,000 babies died in the first year of life.

The widespread idea that modern life is unhealthy is there-fore quite erroneous. Actually it encourages us to be more mobile and thus to keep younger than in the "good old days". We look after our bodies better than ever before and the salutary effects of the sun's rays have been discovered along with vitamins and other constituents of a practical diet. There are grounds enough, and we have by no means exhausted them, to show that men today, on an average, age later and live longer than their forebears. In the last ten years the number of people in the higher age groups has increased considerably. This, according to statistics, means that both the very young and older people can expect a considerably longer lifespan. When one assesses the life-potential of either sex today in a civilised land a 30-year-old has an average expectation of 30 years and a 40-year-old 31 years. The corresponding figures for the year 1880 showed 22 years for a

30-year-old, and 25 years for a 40-year-old. A 50-year-old man today has an average life expectation of 23 years (in 1880 it would have been 18 years). From the age of 60 onwards the figures approach those of the old days—for example, a 90-year-old in 1870 had the same expectation as anyone today who has reached this venerable age. According to statistics they could both live for another two years.

Are there any grounds to suppose that some people will live to be 100 while most others will not? To obtain any accurate information about centenarians has been a very difficult task. Verification of their age is often problematical enough, and the question why they have lived to be so old is even more difficult to answer. Some of these "old-timers" have eaten and drunk their fill while others have been very frugal; some of them swear by spirits and others are teetotal; among them we find smokers and non-smokers, vegetarians and meat-eaters; but very seldom do we find any real reason why in these individual cases the normal span of human life should have been exceeded. In general we have only been able to ascertain that inheritance plays a large part. Insurance company statistics reveal that people whose parents reach a "ripe old age" usually die at a more advanced age than is normal. Furthermore, women have far better prospects than men. A strict survey showed that of 124 persons of over 100 years of age, and whose age was beyond dispute, 83 were women and only 41 were men. According to these figures the presumption is that a woman has double the chance of a man of living to be 100.

WHY DO WOMEN LIVE LONGER THAN MEN?

Anyone who considers this theme would give a snap answer: men take greater risks than women. They work in mines, in factories, in dangerous occupations such as flying . . . and they have to go to war. This is all perfectly true, but it is by no means the sole deciding factor, for at all stages of life the male sex is in greater danger than the female. A preference in favour of the latter already appears in childbirth, where mortality—including stillborn babies—is far greater in males than in females. Countless diseases such as ulcers, gout, and certain cardiac and blood disorders are far more common in men, or in some cases are found only in men; we may instance hæmophilia. Moreover, women are seldom colour-blind and rarely go bald. Members of the "gentle sex" are not nearly so prone to psychic disturbances as men; who are supposed to be spiritually more robust. On an average they suffer far more nervous breakdowns and their suicide rate is higher. The widespread mental disturbance, stuttering, is five times more common in men than in women.

Is there any reason, then, why women should ever have been called the "weaker" sex? Yes and No. Naturally the woman is not as powerful as her mate, for her musculature is far weaker, her bones more fragile, and her physical potential lower. But strength should not be confused with toughness: a woman's powers of resistance to adversities of all kinds is actually far greater. There are scores of anecdotes on the well-known theme that men dramatise the smallest cold in the head whereas the average woman ignores it. Possibly this much-ridiculed behaviour has something to do with the greater sensitivity of the male sex. Women bore privation and the nights of bombing during the Second World War more stoically than men, or at least they recovered more quickly from the effects. They are usually less prone to psychological shock and make a speedier recovery from such afflictions.

Investigations in Germany have shown that countless women could not reply when asked for details of their sufferings during the bombing, their flight from the enemy, of the years of famine after the war. They have a very convenient faculty for forgetting. Things are more difficult for men, who are more inclined to have a nervous breakdown after some shattering experience, or to succumb to intoxication or, in the last extreme, to suicide. The man stores up feelings of displeasure, while the woman forgets them.

The examples we have quoted show clearly enough that the physical and mental powers of resistance of women are greater on the whole than the corresponding powers of the "stronger" sex. Nature never acts without a purpose, so what is the reason for this apparent female privilege? Well, the human race would probably long since have died out had not the female sex possessed from the very start complementary reserves in the shape of special powers of resistance, which were obviously intended as a compensation for the great risk the woman runs when fulfilling her biological task. In the past giving birth meant death for countless mothers. We should not lose sight of the fact that the successful attempts to combat the dreaded puerperal fever were not made until 1847. At that time Ignaz Semmelweis, who has been called the "mother's saviour", recognised that it was caused by an infection. He disinfected the hands of the midwife with chlorine, and this blazed the trail for aseptics and antiseptics. Cases of puerperal fever are rare today in civilised countries, but in the old days it claimed countless mothers. Other dangers common to pregnancy and birth can also be dealt with effectively today, so that a normal birth in highly civilised countries entails very little risk. For this reason alone the average expectation of life of the modern woman has shown a sharp rise.

The converse is easy to prove. Let us take India as an illustration. The birth-rate in that vast and so far undeveloped land is among the highest in the world, and the figure for the average expectation of life of the Indian woman is the lowest. According to the latest statistics, an Indian girl has the prospect of 27 years of life and an Indian boy may reach the age of 33. Here matters are diametrically opposed to those in countries which practise modern hygiene. The biological risk of the woman—heightened by the conditions of a hot climate, and the Indian custom of early marriage—is severe in the extreme, as the figures we have quoted show only too clearly. Under "natural" conditions, therefore, the woman is in greater danger than the man, hence she needs the toughness we have mentioned.

Research into old age continues and no one can forecast what the eventual results will be. It is not a matter of prolonging the lives of as many dotards of ninety to a hundred years of age as possible, and it is very questionable whether this is at all desirable. The greatest suffering in this world does not arise from the natural process of ageing, and death from old age, but from disease and early death before the normal limit of human life has been reached. The first objective is to protect people up to a ripe age from disease and epidemics, and secondly to preserve their mental and physical faculties. It is not the number of years lived that is decisive in making life worth living but the form and content of the years we are allowed to spend as healthy and active individuals. By a rational way of life we can do much to protect ourselves from damage and premature old age. Modern science affords us the possibility of reaching this goal more effectively than our forebears, with the best will in the world, could have done. Moreover, the average life span will probably continue to increase and only the future can tell where the limit lies.

BIOLOGICAL TIME

When we speak of the length of life of some organism we normally calculate it in months, years or decades. At the beginning of this chapter we saw that there are vast differences in this field, some living creatures measuring their life span by days and others by centuries. This already shows that the concept of time in the world of the living is far less rigid and, one might say, less generally valid than it is in the world of physics or astronomy. Thus the apparently unchangeable unit of time, one year, does not mean the same for a small child as for an adult. In the course of a year much more happens to a child than to its parents: it grows, it develops physically and mentally, and its experiences are far more active and varied than they will be later.

In addition to the time recorded by our clocks, which our observatories control with precision instruments, there is another time—biological time. And the clock of life runs differently from the watch on our wrists. Modern biology knows for certain that there is no such thing as a common average experience of time for all living creatures, but each has, according to species, age, environment, etc., a particular inner time, so to speak. For example, in the hibernation of animals it comes almost to a standstill; in fact in certain living creatures the time factor can be almost entirely occluded, namely when they lead a latent obscured life during certain periods of inactivity. The amœba can shrink to a tiny structure in periods of drought and remain in this timeless condition for years, and similar states of "drought sleep" are known in many other organisms. There are certain tapeworms which normally live for a year, but in certain conditions they can live for several decades in a kind of dry rigidity. If they are moistened, their development continues as though nothing had happened. Young trichina complete their life span in a very short time as soon as they reach the intestine of a new host animal, but they can just as well live for thirty years and longer in a state of encystment in their temporary host. Their lifetime begins again then when they can feed on a new host.

We find even more astonishing cases of the relativity of biological concepts of time in the seeds of plants. From lengthy experiment we know that the germinative power of seeds normally lasts for a few years, and at the most a few decades. In the *papilionaceæ* this capacity is higher and can amount to eighty years. The well known lotus flower, which is sacred in East Asia, must be judged by a completely "other" time standard, for seeds of this plant from cultivations 1,000 years old and more have been found in peat and were still active.

The reproductive cells of lower plants, the spores of mosses, algæ and fungi, are almost ageless and their germinative power is apparently unlimited. A Soviet expedition brought back samples of the frozen soil of northern Siberia which had not thawed since the Ice Age. When investigated they were found to contain a wealth of spores that had not lost their potency after remaining inactive for thousands of years. Similar records in age will be found among the bacteria. On analysing bits of masonry from ancient buildings, bacteria, which had remained alive for well over a thousand years, were found inside the stones. Further confirmation was provided by samples of rubble from the temples of the Peruvian Indians, for inside the bricks, baked 1,500 years ago, living bacteria were also discovered.

McCay's previously-mentioned experiments with rats point conclusively to the relativity of biological time, for his experimental animals aged far slower than normal rats and their span of life was artificially prolonged. Incidentally, the span of life can also be artificially shortened—in other words, the clock of life can be made to run faster. Loeb carried out experiments of this kind on flies. He kept them for long periods in abnormally high temperature conditions, with the result that they aged faster and died earlier than is usual in the ca of these insects. If, on the contrary, primitive living creatures are kept at very low temperatures their span of life can be considerably prolonged.

THE CLOCK OF OUR LIFE

In men no change in their inner time can be achieved with such simple methods, with the corresponding influence on their length of life. The rhythm of our lives is difficult to alter, and it alters for reasons that we hardly know. At certain times we grow old more quickly and at other times more slowly. As a basic rule we can say that the life processes in childhood are very rapid, that they slow down in youth, and that they reach the slowest possible tempo in old age. Our life-clock can be read by our pulse beats. From the 120 beats per minute in the baby they decrease to 60 in the dotard. If we reckon the time of childhood and old age in solar years, the former appears comparatively short and the latter long. In the inner time units read from the clock of life it is just the reverse. Childhood is very long and old age short. We know this from repeated experience—our childhood days seem very long, while as we grow older they appear to fly. On the basis of many experiments on this interesting question a denominator has been struck which shows that time passes five times more swiftly for a 60-year-old than for a 10-year-old.

Moreover, the biological time of the individual depends largely upon his constitution and also upon the sum total of his basically conditioned qualities. At some time or other we have all noticed that many men of fifty are very young with regard to their physical and mental capacities, whereas others, long before reaching this age, are worn out and have aged prematurely. Modern research has pursued this question with exact methods and with very important results. *A priori* it was necessary to find the most objective test for the physical overall condition of subjects at various ages. A particularly suitable age index turned out to be the cicatrization speed of superficial wounds. When a five-year-old child has a surface skin wound of ten square centimetres it normally heals in six and a-half days. In the case of a man of forty the same wound needs on an average eighteen days to close, and in the case of a sixty-year-old thirty-two days. This "cicatrization index" has been tested on thousands of experimental subjects in war and peace, and it invariably showed the same average figures.

At the same time, further tests have revealed that there is a high percentage of exceptions—of people whose cicatrization index figure does not confirm to their age. In these exceptions, which amount to between 10% and 15%, wounds heal faster or slower than the age would indicate. Here the "psychological age", which has nothing to do with the age of birth, has to be taken into account. This individually varying course of biological time shows that many people are comparatively younger and others considerably older than their actual number of years. In them the body substance also ages faster or slower than is normal and the cicatrization index confirms ancient experience in a scientific manner. It can be summed up by the old expression "a man is as old as he feels".

Naturally these exceptions are only a deviation from a norm which was laid down for men, animals or plants, according to their species. The fly ages more swiftly than the parrot. The course of ageing in man has naturally been the subject of exhaustive research, and it has been found that the muscle power reaches its peak between the ages of 20 and 30 and from then on slowly but surely decreases. Considerably later comes the first slowing down of the heart functions, while the lungs reach the peak of their capacity at the age of 35, with a subsequent decline. Many of the manifestations of age already appear in youth, others very late. In practice each component part of the body ages in its own prescribed individual manner.

Scientists are all in agreement, but they have no final answer to the question: is there a kind of "conductor" of the ageing processes? In other words, does the decline of certain organs or bodily functions provide the tempo for ageing, to be followed by all the other phenomena of old age? Detailed research has begun on this practical but very significant problem in the United States and the Soviet Union. It has been found that we must look upon ageing in higher life as a process that we may one day be able to retard but can never really halt.

TO GROW OLD—TO REMAIN YOUNG

Man, in the course of his history, has realised many of hi important and unimportant wishes: his life progressively gro more "comfortable" and ever more effective measures are being discovered to protect us from the diseases and the rigours of Nature. But the oldest dream of mankind, the dream of eternal youth, has never been fulfilled. Countless generations have dreamed of it, seeking in vain the "elixir of life" or "fountain of youth". And what of today? Our modern age at least refrains from begging this question with quick remedies and explores it with scientific method. The first serious attempts at artificial rejuvenation of men and animals were carried out with the aid of sex hormones. Thyroid glands of young animals were grafted into dogs, guinea pigs, and rats showing outward signs of age, in order to revive the flagging production of sex hormones of the latter. The same purpose was served by ligature of the spermatic duct in old animals, thereby reviving the activities of the testicles.

Such methods achieved notable success at the outset. A few days after the operation the experimental animals showed clear signs of rejuvenation throughout the organism. Their fur became smoother and thicker and the lost sexual urge returned. But by and large all these efforts, begun with so much enthusiasm, came to naught. The effect of the interference in most cases was of short duration—in dogs, on an average, only a few weeks. By frequent repetition the animals could be rejuvenated again, but soon there was no effect, and finally in every case there was a steep decline in vitality which led quickly to death. Rejuvenation therefore had been achieved only at the expense of the last reserves of these experimental animals, and it was more in the nature of a whipping-up of their strength than of a genuine renewal of the ageing body. Steinach, Voronoff and others tried out similar rejuvenating methods on ageing people, but after a time no more was heard of these sensational experiments, for the effect of the stimuli in the case of humans also lasted but a short time, only finally to prove ineffectual. So far there is no single recorded case of a "rejuvenated" patient reaching a higher age than he would have done without such intervention.

Soviet biologists, in particular A. Bogomoletz, have blazed a new trail in the battle against the onset of old age. He started from the premise that the process of ageing, regardless of its use, has the effect of a slow decline in the vitality of our body cells. In the course of time they become less capable of functioning; they degenerate and lose water. Bogomoletz works with a serum deriving from the cells of the human pancreas and bone marrow. The serum is used in very small quantities but reacts favourably on the human body and above all on the cells of the connective tissue. Since this tissue is of great importance to the overall condition of the body, Bogomoletz saw in his serum the possibility of refreshing the organism, as it were, of protecting it from disease and postponing its lapse into senility. The hope for prolongation of life did not mature, but the serum appears in certain suitable cases to arrest the exhaustion-condition of the physical functions and to retard the process of old age. But this serum is unfortunately not a genuine rejuvenating remedy.

The no less controversial meristematic therapy is ideal for combating certain diseases but is not a method of rejuvenation. It seems highly improbable that we will ever succeed in making men really "younger" than they were before undergoing treatments such as those we have just discussed. Nature does not make things so simple for us and we have to help ourselves. This consists above all in following an intelligent diet which supplies the needs of the body in every respect and avoids any excess, particularly of fats. Further, as we all know, physical exercise, regular walks in the fresh air, and moderation in the pleasure-giving toxins will preserve the resilience of the body. Simple and natural as these constant recommendations are, the less they are followed. American doctors, in a recent public appeal, have pointed out that the general physical condition of young men called up for military service is far from satisfactory. The cause given was the widespread renunciation of active sport and even of walking. The car, of course, plays a prominent part in the perpetual search for comfort, and in Europe too the constant increase in motoring makes more and more people "spare" their natural tools for locomotion—namely, the legs.

MENTAL EFFORT PROLONGS LIFE

Modern research has proved conclusively that work has a prolonging effect on life. If for some reason a person gives u all further professional or other activities on reaching retirem age he will on the average die earlier than he would have done had he carried on with an occupation appropriate to his individual strength. Whether the activity is of a physical or mental nature does not (at least in principle) determine its significance or its effect on the life span of the worker, apart of course from particularly heavy and unhealthy occupations. There are very differently constituted groups of professions whose members have a similar mortality standard—for example, doctors and commercial travellers, leather-workers and chemists, artists and carpenters—although these callings entail partly mental and partly physical work. But it is another matter altogether when a man who has grown old renounces with passive resignation the strong stimuli which are provided by any intelligent form of activity, whether he practises it or not.

If someone has the misfortune to break an arm or a leg the limb in question has to be set in plaster. It is therefore "retired" and the muscles give no further support. They atrophy— a degeneration of the tissue, which has been reduced to inactivity, sets in. When the plaster is removed it is some time before the patient recovers the full use of his arm or leg. Now if an elderly man does not exert his brain enough exactly the same thing happens to him as to the limb in plaster. This can be proved exactly. The well-known German brain specialist, Vogt, recently dissected the brain of a man who died at the age of fifty, and to his surprise found that it was ten years "older" than it should have been for his age. The case history revealed that the man had been an idler for many years who had ceased to work at a profession or to indulge in any other intelligent form of activity. This led to the reduction and to the final collapse of many of the neurons in his brain.

His case is by no means exceptional. It has been proved by Vogt himself and other specialists that a brain not only ages quicker but even degenerates when it is not given enough to do. Our brain is so constituted that its functioning, its sanguinification, and in consequence its whole metabolism must be stimulated by demands being made upon it. According to modern brain specialists, it follows that general activation of the neurons retards their ageing and benefits their capacity. To put it in a nutshell: "thinking spares the brain".

This knowledge is of particular importance and should be

accepted by everyone, not only by old men. Biologists have
described man as a "thinking animal", as a creature whose
special imprint and development has always been and will be
decisively determined by the brain, in particular by the cerebrum. When we compare the weight of the brain with the
weight of the body a remarkable fact emerges. Our "thinking"
organ, as regards the pure mass of cerebrum, exceeds sevenfold
that of the most intelligent of all animals, the chimpanzee.
Whereas in young primates the weight of the brain increases
insignificantly, the neurons of the newborn human baby have
not yet matured. The weight of a baby's brain doubles during
the first year of its life, finally reaching three times the weight at
birth. This is also why the young of animals are far more dex-
terous than the almost helpless baby and the small child. But
to offset this, man's slowly-developing brain possesses a stability
which enables him, by comparison, to reach a very great
age.

If *Homo Sapiens* is a thinking animal, and if the thinking decisively determines both his way of life and his longevity, it
must in practise have very important consequences for elderly
and old men. Since any activity slows down the ageing
process of the neurons, while inactivity hastens it, we must
radically revise our ideas about the quiet and uneventful
existence to be led by the old-age pensioner and those in the
twilight of their life. When men or women retire completely
from their work and in the true sense of the words "put their
feet up" they renounce that important brain-activation of which
we spoke, and by so doing shorten their lives. It is therefore
highly desirable that as many people as possible should be
allowed to work to well over the present-day retirement age, if
they so wish, and if their mental and physical capacities warrant
it. Unusually excessive demands do not, as was earlier believed,
entail a premature "wear and tear" of the ganglion cells of the
brain, but rather the opposite. The German specialist, Ehrenberg, pointed out that there is a vital difference between the
thinking organ, the brain, and the purely functional pump
apparatus of the heart. Overtaxing of an ageing heart is harmful, but taxing of the brain can prove useful.

The need for a change of outlook in this field has been rece
nised by the Americans, who are far less conservative

traditional than Europeans, and for some time now they have put the theory into practise. Daily experience teaches us that an elderly worker, perhaps even a senior clerk, often finds great difficulty in finding a new post once he has lost his own for some reason. In the U.S.A. it is different, because beyond the Atlantic there is no prejudice against employing elderly workers. They are given a chance. If they prove satisfactory all is well, if not they are sacked. In practice this attitude, according to the latest statistics, has resulted in more than half the men in the U.S.A in the age group 65 to 69 being employed. Even in the 70 to 74 group 40% still do a paid job, although it is usually very light work for only a few hours of the day.

Naturally the corresponding figures for women are much lower. Only 13% of them are capable of working over the age of 65. American women, however, never retire, but occupy themselves with every possible social or other activity. They go for long voyages, arrange lectures, and are constantly active in their women's clubs. Obviously this suits them, for statistics place the American woman at the top of the scale as regards expectation of life. It does not really matter if an elderly man works professionally or at some hobby. What really matters is that in some way or another the most sensitive and at the same time most enduring cells of our body, the brain neurons, are given sufficient work to do.

TWO LIFE STAGES

Our lives consist of two clearly separate phases, one somatically and one psychically determined. The first stage brings physical development and education, followed by procreation and care of the progeny! During this phase man, by developing his cerebrum, is preparing for the second stage—the decades of intellectual maturity and a fulfilment of the highest specifically human tasks. Whereas the curve of the purely physiological capacity is already on the decline, the intellectual powers increase, and often reach their optimum, in the middle of the period of physical degeneration. Statistics of intellectual achievements show that this can be accurately checked chronologically. Under review were the masterpieces of poets and composers, particularly outstanding work of scientists and great deeds of statesmen. The following table shows the most productive year of life, according to various professions:

Chemists and physicists	41 years
Poets and dramatists	44 years
Novelists	46 years
Army commanders and travellers . .	47 years
Composers and actors	48 years
Social reformers and publicists . . .	51 years
Statesmen and doctors	52 years
Philosophers	54 years
Astronomers, mathematicians, satirists and humorists	56 years
Historians	57 years
Lawyers and naturalists	58 years

Far beyond the perceptible limits of these statistics lie the outstanding "late works", showing intellectual achievements in all fields. Titian painted one of his finest pictures, *The Battle of Lepanto*, at the age of 98, Verdi composed *Otello* at 74, the German historian, von Ranke, began his famous *History of the World* at the age of 80, and Michael Angelo wrote his immortal sonnets at the age of 79.

In view of his intellectual achievements it would appear that man was intended to reach a great age, the actual significance of which we have so far badly misunderstood. This is not altogether surprising, for in the long history of the human race only a few individuals were able to enjoy the second phase of their lives. Until the last century the average expectation of life was below 40 years. In our century for the first time man, thanks to his increasing knowledge, can penetrate the secrets of his own corporeality, combat diseases, and finally put an end to the weaknesses of his biological status. The result will be a swift increase in the average life span, which has already doubled since the days of our grandparents.

Thus for the first time the attainment of great and very great ages will no longer be, as in the past, an exception but even the rule. Taking the long view, this means, in spite of the many problems still to be solved, the start of a new and positiv development. The greater the accumulation of knowledge, a the more complicated the achievements become that are demanded in all fields of our existence, the more imperative will be the need for that wealth of experience and education which will eventually grant us a long life. If science succeeds in bringing more and more people to a great age with their physical and intellectual health preserved, there is every prospect that at least a large number of the species, *Homo Sapiens*, will not only be "knowledgeable" but also "wise".

Index of Names

Index